**CLASSIC RESEARCHES IN GENERAL CHEMISTRY**

Series Editor · HAROLD HART, MICHIGAN STATE UNIVERSITY

THE

CLASSIC RESEARCHES IN GENERAL CHEMISTRY

J. J. LAGOWSKI · THE UNIVERSITY OF TEXAS

STRUCTURE

OF ATOMS

HOUGHTON MIFFLIN COMPANY · BOSTON

NEW YORK · ATLANTA · GENEVA, ILL. · DALLAS · PALO ALTO

To J

Cover photo: Individual atoms show up clearly in
this field-ion microscope image of a single crystal
tungsten point. The microscope provides an unparal-
leled magnification of greater than one million times
which allows detailed studies of surface structure never
before possible. (Courtesy of Dr. Erwin W. Mueller,
Pennsylvania State University.)

EDITOR'S INTRODUCTION

The accelerated pace of scientific discovery which characterizes our time has necessarily eliminated the historical approach to the study of science. Elementary texts in chemistry and physics cannot detail the often tortuous arguments, hypotheses, and experiments upon which currently accepted theories and facts are built. The result is often simply an outline of where we stand today, with only a few cogent arguments or supporting experiments enumerated. During the continuous distillation and condensation (which, indeed, are necessary to prevent elementary texts from becoming encyclopedic), many discoveries, when described in textbook fashion, lose their freshness.

But scientific discovery is a thrilling and exciting process, and a zest for it should be imparted to the beginning student. This series of paperbacks was initiated with the view that much might be done toward this end if the beginner could read about key discoveries in science in the words of the men who wrote of them. The research worker who contributes to the advancing front of science must read of discoveries as they appear in the scientific journals; he cannot wait until they become the subject matter of textbooks. It would seem advisable, then, to introduce the neophyte to the original literature as early in his scientific career as possible. The difficulty encountered in doing this lies in the student's lack of a suitable background necessary for him to profit from being turned loose amongst the journals with a list of references to read. Indeed, he may be dissuaded altogether from the sciences if subjected to such a "trial by fire" procedure. It was therefore decided that original papers, or portions thereof, be selected and presented with sufficient editorial comment to set the stage for each paper and to clarify passages which might be troublesome to the beginner. For the most part, the great scientists are allowed to speak for themselves.

The non-science major who takes a year of college chemistry or physics as part of his liberal education will find that this little book makes fascinating reading not only because the scientists come alive on its pages, but also because he can learn much about the use of logic and scientific method. But foremost, this book will make excellent supplementary reading for the professional student of chemistry or physics who wants to understand in greater detail the basis for our modern theory of the structure of atoms.

HAROLD HART

v

Today's description of the atom is the result of thousands of experiments, many of them unsuccessful or imperfectly devised, and numerous suggestions; the development of this concept can be likened to a jigsaw puzzle. Many pieces of the puzzle fall readily into place, but periodically there is a crucial piece missing. It is these crucial pieces with which we concern ourselves here. It should be emphasized, however, that the puzzle would be just as incomplete if one of the lesser pieces, rather than a crucial piece, were missing, for very often the importance of an experiment is determined by the time at which it was performed.

The development of the present ideas concerning the structure of atoms could be traced along many different paths. A historical development, often quoting the investigators' original words, has been attempted in an effort to give the reader an appreciation of the information available at the time a crucial piece of work was reported. This approach to the subject is intended to emphasize the brilliance of many important discoveries by focusing the reader's attention on the reasoning employed in context with the data available from other investigations. The explanations of many of the experimental results that are apparent to us today were not necessarily so obvious at the time the results were obtained. It is impossible to quote in their entirety all of the important papers involved in the development of atomic structure in a volume of this size, and therefore only selected passages from the original papers are presented. For those interested in reading the original articles references are given in the footnotes. In several instances a choice had to be made between excerpts from the same paper and/or from different papers; selection of the excerpt quoted in this volume is dictated by the line of reasoning embarked upon, although other passages can be employed to illustrate the point involved if taken individually.

The author also wishes to express his appreciation to all the people at the Houghton Mifflin Company and at The University of Texas who have assisted him in this project; to Professor Harold Hart for the helpful suggestions he offered after reading the manuscript at the penultimate stage; and to his wife for her many constructive criticisms and her constant encouragement.

J. J. L.
Austin, Texas

CONTENTS

CONTENTS

CHAPTER 1

Evidence for the
Existence of Atoms

The history of the atomic theory can be divided into three periods as a matter of convenience: the ancient period (450–320 B.C.), the period beginning immediately after the middle ages (1600–1850), and the modern period (the last hundred years). The philosophers of the ancient period concerned themselves with pure thought, ideas, and reasoning. The 1900-year interval between the first and second of these periods was one of stagnation for scientific investigation and theories. Although evidence for the existence of the atom was gathered in the second of these periods, it was not until the last hundred years or so that the structure of the atom has been elucidated.

Throughout the course of history matter has been considered to be either continuous or discontinuous. The theory of the continuous nature of matter postulates that matter is homogeneous and may be subdivided *without limit*, each unit of subdivision maintaining the same properties as all other smaller or larger units. On the other hand, theories of the particulate nature of matter, i.e. atomic theories, permit the subdivision of matter into a basic unit (an atom) without effecting a change in its properties; according to these theories subdivision of matter beyond the atomic level yields other particles with profoundly different properties of characteristics. Although the atomic concept is generally credited to Greek philosophers, there are indications that an atomic theory had been developed by Hindu philosophers earlier.

EARLIEST ATOMIC CONCEPTS

The first explicit description of the atomic hypothesis is present in the writings

1

of Democritus (Demokritos) of Abdera,[1] and to him is usually given the credit for its origination, although similar but incompletely developed ideas are found in the writings of several other earlier Greek philosophers. Democritus considered all matter to be composed of atoms of the four "elements" — earth, air, fire, and water — which were in continual random motion in a vacuum. Thus, Democritus conceived of the atomic theory as well as the kinetic theory! These atoms possessed a certain physical size and had a characteristic geometric shape. When mixed in the correct proportions, the atoms of the four elements produced all other substances. Democritus' atoms were the ultimate particles of matter, and he did not think that they could be further subdivided. This atomistic philosophy of matter was accepted and modified by Plato, a pupil of Socrates, but Plato's pupil Aristotle[2] rejected the atomic hypothesis and postulated that matter was homogeneous and indefinitely divisible. Unfortunately, Aristotelian philosophy maintained an overpowering influence on contemporary thought until the sixteenth century, and the atomic theory was not considered seriously by most philosophers during this period.

It is important to note that the two opposing theories describing matter were originally ideas concerning how different philosophers thought matter should be constructed, and the rise and fall of these theories in ancient times occurred because of a change in the way people thought. Very little experimental work that was done during this period, e.g. Hero of Alexandria's study of steam as reported in his work *Pneumatics*, indicated that matter was particulate, but this evidence could not compete with the powerful influence of Aristotelian thought which dominated men's minds until about the early seventeenth century. As products of reason, both Aristotle's and Democritus' models of matter were acceptable; however, as we shall see, the modern atomic theory is a product of reason guided by experimental observations.

The Rise of Experimentalism

Prior to the sixteenth century the alchemists, in striving toward their various goals, i.e. transmutation of metals and discovery of the philosopher's stone, uncovered new substances, and new ideas developed which required modification of Aristotle's model of matter. It was Francis Bacon[3] and Pierre

[1] Democritus (460–370 B.C.): A Greek philosopher who extended the "mechanistic" philosophy of his teacher Leucippus. The atomic theory is a portion of Democritus' philosophy and was based on reason rather than experiment.

[2] Aristotle (384–322 B.C.): A Greek philosopher, a student of Plato, and teacher of Alexander the Great. Many of his ideas have survived the passage of time, but his suggestion that matter is infinite and the powerful influence of his ideas retarded the use of the experimental method.

[3] Francis Bacon, Baron Verulam, Viscount St. Albans (1561–1626): Jurist, philosopher, and Lord Chancellor of England under James I. Although not noted as an experimental scientist, his system of inductive logic, described in his book *Novum Organum*, is the basis of modern scientific thinking.

Gassendi[4] who revived the atomic theory of Democritus and adapted it to the experimental information available at the time. Two streams of information gave support to the atomic theory. The behavior of gaseous matter could be explained on the basis of the existence of molecules or atoms, and unfortunately the distinction between these two designations was not always made clear. The main body of information to support the suggestion that matter is composed of atoms was obtained from the painstakingly gathered, quantitative weight relationships in chemical reactions.

As a result of his experiments on the calcination (heating in air) of mercury and the decomposition of mercuric oxide into oxygen and mercury, Antoine Lavoisier[5] laid the foundation for the law of conservation of mass in chemical reactions as well as presented the correct interpretation of the phenomenon of combustion. Lavoisier also suggested the first working definition of an element. The concept of elemental substances had its origin in philosophy, but Lavoisier considered substances which could not be resolved chemically into simpler substances as elements. This concept placed the burden of proof on the chemist, for, if he were not clever in his experiments, the elemental nature of certain substances would never be known. Indeed, Lavoisier himself included lime (CaO), alumina (Al_2O_3), and silica (SiO_2) in his list of elemental substances. Proust[6] successfully established the validity of the law of constant composition in the early nineteenth century after the eminent French chemist Berthollet[7] had suggested (incorrectly) that elements underwent chemical reaction in an unlimited number of proportions. Berthollet probably reached the wrong conclusions because he did not distinguish between homogeneous mixtures and

[4] Pierre Gassendi (1592–1655): French priest, philosopher, scientist, and mathematician. Although he initially embraced Aristotelian philosophy, he began to question its precepts after reading of the discoveries of Galileo and Kepler. He added very little experimental work to scientific knowledge, and his greatest contribution was that in his writings he continually stressed the importance of experimental research. In this respect he was Bacon's ally.

[5] Antoine Laurent Lavoisier (1743–1794): Often called the founder of modern chemistry. By employing quantitative methods of experimentation he correctly described the process of combustion, enunciated the law of conservation of matter, and demonstrated that air is a mixture. With the aid of Fourcroy, Berthollet, and Morveau, he formulated the system of chemical nomenclature in use today. He met his death at the guillotine during the Reign of Terror of the French Republic on the charge of "adding water to the peoples' tobacco."

[6] Joseph Louis Proust (1754–1826): Professor of Chemistry at Salamanca University and later Director of the Royal Laboratory at Madrid. The law of definite composition was established by Proust in the course of an eight-year controversy with Berthollet; the latter believed that chemical combinations could occur to give products with any given proportion of constituents. Proust's work laid the foundation for the law of multiple proportions.

[7] Claude Louis Berthollet (1748–1822): Professor at the École Normale. Born in humble circumstances, Berthollet filled many responsible positions in the government of France and eventually became a Count of the Empire under Napoleon. His belief that two or more elements could combine in varying proportions was the source of a long controversy with Proust during which the latter established the law of definite composition. Among his chemical accomplishments are the introduction of "Eau de Javelle" for bleaching purposes, the establishment of the composition of ammonia, hydrogen cyanide, and hydrogen sulfide, and the revision (with Lavoisier) of chemical nomenclature.

compounds. In a sense, Proust's establishment of the law of definite proportions was a triumph of the concept that chemical reactions are orderly over the suggestion that chemical reactions are unpredictable. Proust showed that copper carbonate contained the same proportion by weight of its constituent elements regardless of whether this compound was obtained naturally or was prepared in the laboratory. Moreover, the proportions were constant and independent of the natural source of this compound, so long as the compound was pure. In the course of establishing the law of definite proportions, Proust also collected data which illustrated the law of multiple proportions although he did not formulate it as such. This task fell to John Dalton,[8] a man noted for his keen insight rather than for his experimental prowess.

DALTON'S ATOM

Although an atomic theory[9] had been suggested previously by Newton to explain the behavior of gases, it was Dalton who first explained the facts of chemical combination by assuming that all reactions involved the union or separation of atoms. Dalton had used the atomic theory as applied to gases when he postulated the law of partial pressures,[10] and it was natural for him to extend these ideas to the realm of chemical combinations. DALTON'S chain of reasoning is best described by his own words.

▼   "There are three distinctions in the kinds of bodies, or three states, which have more especially claimed the attention of philosophical chemists, namely, those which are marked by the terms elastic fluids, liquids, and solids. A very familiar instance is exhibited to us in water, of a body, which in certain circumstances, is capable of assuming all the three states. In steam we recognize a perfectly elastic fluid, in water a perfect liquid, and in ice, a complete solid.

"These observations have tacitly led to the conclusion which seems universally adopted, that all bodies of sensible magnitude whether liquid or solid, are constituted of a vast number of extremely small particles, or atoms of matter, bound together by a force of attraction, which is more or less powerful according to circumstances, and which, as it endeavors to pre-

---

[8] John Dalton (1766–1844): A Quaker school teacher in Manchester, England. His study of gases and their chemical composition led to the formulation of the law of multiple proportions and to an assignment of relative combining weights for the elements. The formulation of the atomic theory and its application to chemical combinations were his greatest contributions to science.

[9] In the earlier theories, no distinction was made between atoms and molecules, and the word atom was used to designate the smallest *particle* of matter.

[10] Dalton's law of partial pressures states that each gas in a mixture of gases exerts a pressure independent of the presence of the other gases. Thus, the total pressure of the gases comprising the mixture is the sum of the partial pressures of each gas.

vent their separation, is very properly called in that view, attraction of cohesion; but as it collects them from a dispersed state (as from steam into water) it is called attraction of aggregation, or more simply, affinity.

"Whether the ultimate particles of a body, such as water, are all alike, that is, of the same figure, weight, etc. is a question of some importance. From what is known, we have no reason to apprehend a diversity in these particulars: if it does exist in water, it must equally exist in the elements constituting water, namely, hydrogen and oxygen. Now it is scarcely possible to conceive how the aggregates of dissimilar particles should be so uniformly the same. If some of the particles of water were heavier than others — if a parcel of the liquid on any occasion were constituted principally of these heavier particles, it must be supposed to affect the specific gravity of the mass, a circumstance not known. Similar observations may be made on other substances; therefore we may conclude that the ultimate particles of all homogeneous bodies are perfectly alike in weight, figure, etc. in other words, every particle of water is like every other particle of water; every particle of hydrogen is like every other particle of hydrogen."[11] ▲

These ideas are further extended to include chemical combinations.

▼   "Having been long accustomed to make meteorological observations, and to speculate upon the nature and constitution of the atomsphere, it often struck me with wonder how a compound atmosphere, or a mixture of two or more elastic fluids, should constitute apparently a homogeneous mass, or one in all mechanical relations agreeing with a simple atmosphere.

"Newton had demonstrated clearly in the 23rd Prop. of Book II. of the 'Principia' that an elastic fluid is constituted of small particles or atoms of matter which repel each other by a force increasing in proportion as their distance diminishes. But modern discoveries having ascertained that the atmosphere contains three or more elastic fluids of different specific gravities, it did not appear to me how this proposition of Newton's would apply to a case of which he, of course, could have no idea. The same difficulty occurred to Dr. Priestley, who discovered this compound nature of the atmosphere. He could not conceive why the oxygen gas, being specifically heaviest, should not form a distinct stratum of air at the bottom of the atmosphere, and the azotic gas one at the top of the atmosphere. Some chemists upon the Continent — I believe, the French — found a solution of this difficulty (as they apprehended). It was chemical affinity. One species of gas was held in solution by the other; and this compound in its turn dissolved water — hence evaporation, rain, etc. This opinion of air dissolving water had long before been the prevailing one, and naturally paved the way for the reception of that

[11] JOHN DALTON, *New System of Chemical Philosophy* (London: 1842), p. 142.

which followed — of one kind of air dissolving another. It was objected that there was no decisive marks of chemical union when one kind of air was mixed with another. The answer was, that the affinity was of a very slight kind, not of that energetic cast that is observable in most other cases. I may add, by-the-bye, that this is now, or has been till lately, I believe, the prevailing doctrine in most of the chemical schools in Europe. In order to reconcile — or, rather, adapt — this chemical theory of the atmosphere to the Newtonian doctrine of repulsive atoms or particles, I set to work to combine my atoms upon paper. I took an atom of water, another of oxygen, and another of azote, brought them together, and threw around them an atmosphere of heat, as per diagram."[12, 13]   ▲

Dalton goes on to describe how various combinations of oxygen, water, and nitrogen "atoms"[14] could give compounds; thus he clearly postulated that chemical reactions involved the combination of minute particles.

Each atom of a chemical substance has a characteristic mass, and, although the absolute mass could not be determined (at the time), DALTON attempted to determine the relative mass of all elemental substances according to the following argument.

▼   "When any body exists in the elastic state its ultimate particles are separated from each other to a much greater distance than in any other state; each particle occupies the centre of a comparatively large sphere, and supports its dignity by keeping all the rest, which by their gravity or otherwise are disposed to encroach upon it, at a respectful distance. When we attempt to conceive the number of particles in an atmosphere, it is somewhat like attempting to conceive the number of stars in the universe; we are confounded by the thought. But if we limit the subject, by taking a given volume of any gas, we seem persuaded that, let the divisions be ever so minute, the number of particles must be finite; just as in a given space of the universe the number of stars and planets cannot be infinite.

"Chemical analysis and synthesis go no further than to the separation of particles one from another, and to their reunion. No new creation or destruction of matter is within the reach of chemical agency. We might as well attempt to introduce a new planet into the solar system, or to annihilate one already in existence, as to create or destroy a particle of hydrogen. All the changes we can produce consist in separating particles that are in a state of cohesion or combination, and joining those that were previously at a distance.

[12] The early name for nitrogen was azote.
[13] As quoted by Sir Henry Roscoe in *John Dalton and the Rise of Modern Chemistry* (London: Cassell and Company, Ltd., 1895), p. 131.
[14] Dalton used the term "atom" in his writing to mean the smallest individual particle of a sample of matter (*vide infra*).

"In all chemical investigations it has justly been considered an important object to ascertain the relative weights of the samples which constitute a compound. But unfortunately the inquiry has terminated here; whereas from the relative weights in the mass, the relative weights of the ultimate particles or atoms of the bodies might have been inferred, from which their number and weight in various other compounds would appear, in order to assist and to guide future investigations, and to correct their results. Now it is one great object of this work, to show the importance and advantage of ascertaining the relative weights of the ultimate particles both of simple and compound bodies, the number of simple elementary particles which constitute one compound particle, and the number of less compound particles which enter into the formation of one more compound particle.

"If there are two bodies, A and B, which are disposed to combine, the following is the order in which combination may take place, beginning with the most simple: namely —

1 atom of A + 1 atom of B = 1 atom of C, binary,
1 " " A + 2 atoms " B = 1 " " D, ternary,
2 atoms " A + 1 atom " B = 1 " " E, ternary,
1 atom " A + 3 atoms " B = 1 " " F, quaternary,
3 atoms " A + 1 atom " B = 1 " " G, quaternary."[15] ▲

Dalton's "relative atomic weights" were obtained from the analysis of compounds containing hydrogen or oxygen; it was assumed that the molecules of the compounds employed contained one atom of each element. From the proportions of hydrogen and oxygen in water, and the arbitrary assignment of one unit of weight to hydrogen, the "relative atomic weight" of oxygen was found to be 6.5. He was then able to determine the "relative atomic weights" of other atoms by analyzing the compounds they formed with either hydrogen or oxygen; some of the results of this process appear in Table 1.

TABLE 1

Dalton's "Relative Atomic Weights"

Element	Value	
	Dalton	Present
Hydrogen	1	1
Oxygen	6.5	7.94
Nitrogen	5	4.64
Carbon	5.4	6

[15] *New System of Chemical Philosophy*, p. 212.

TABLE 2

The Law of Multiple Proportions Applied to
Carbon Monoxide and Carbon Dioxide

	Percentage composition	parts of C 1 part of O	parts of O 1 part of C
Carbon monoxide			
C	43.5	0.78	1.3
O	56.5		
Carbon dioxide			
C	27.8	0.39	2.6
O	72.2		

It will be recognized that Dalton's method of determining "relative atomic weights" yields the equivalent weights of the elements. Dalton's "error," apart from the experimental difficulties which account for the discrepancies in Table 1, was in the assumption that the compounds he used contained only one atom of each element. This difficulty was readily apparent, however, since two values of the "relative atomic weight" were obtained for many elements. For example, carbon formed two oxides. According to Dalton, 5.4 parts of carbon reacted with 7 parts of oxygen to form one oxide, but the same amount of carbon was found to be combined with 14 parts of oxygen in the other oxide. Thus, carbon could have a "relative atomic weight" of either 5.4 or 2.7 depending upon the oxide chosen for analysis. This example also illustrates the law of multiple proportions[16] which arose from Dalton's atomic theory (rather than vice versa as is usually supposed). As indicated previously, Proust was aware that some elements form two different binary compounds, but, since his results were reported in terms of percentage composition rather than in reference to the same amount of one of the elements, the regularity expressed by the law of multiple proportions was not evident. These relationships are illustrated in Table 2 by using Dalton's data.

The key to understanding the discrepancies in Dalton's theory was provided by Gay-Lussac[17] when he announced the law of combining volumes. After studying a number of reactions that involved gaseous reactants and/or products, Gay-Lussac concluded that "compounds of gaseous substances[18] with each

[16] The law of multiple proportions states that when two elements combine to form more than one compound, the several weights of one element that combine with a fixed weight of the second are in the ratio of small whole numbers.

[17] Joseph Louis Gay-Lussac (1778–1850): Professor at the Paris École Polytechnique. In addition to his studies on the combining volumes of gaseous products and/or reactants, and his investigation into the effect of temperature on the volume of a gas, Gay-Lussac is credited with the isolation of boron. He made the first detailed study of iodine and cyanogen with the aid of Thénard.

[18] Measured under the same conditions of temperature and pressure.

other are always formed in very simple ratios, so that representing one of the terms by unity, the other is 1, or 2, or at the most 3."[19]

AVOGADRO'S HYPOTHESIS

It was Avogadro[20] who applied these results to Dalton's theory and suggested a method for determining the relative weights of molecules and atoms. The distinction between atoms of elements, which could combine to form molecules of elements, and molecules in general, was not made by Dalton; his "atoms" were the particles which gave bulk matter its properties. Unfortunately, most of these particles were in reality molecules. AVOGADRO's introduction to his classic paper contains the hypothesis which permits the calculation of relative molecular weights.

▼   "M. Gay-Lussac has shown in an interesting Memoir (Mémoires de la Société d'Arcueil, Tome II.) that gases always unite in a very simple proportion by volume, and that when the result of the union is a gas, its volume also is very simply related to those of its components. But the quantitative proportions of substances in compounds seem only to depend on the relative number of molecules[21] which combine, and on the number of composite molecules which result. It must then be admitted that very simple relations also exist between the volumes of gaseous substances and the numbers of simple or compound molecules which form them. The first hypothesis to present itself in this connection, and apparently even the only admissible one, is the supposition that the number of integral molecules in any gases is always the same for equal volumes, or always proportional to the volumes. Indeed, if we were to suppose that the number of molecules contained in a given volume were different for different gases, it would scarcely be possible to conceive that the law regulating the distance of molecules could give in all cases relations so simple as those which the facts just detailed compel us to acknowledge between the volume and the number of molecules.

[19] Foundations of the Molecular Theory, Alembic Club Reprints, No. 4 (Edinburgh: Oliver and Boyd, 1923), p. 24.

[20] Amadeo Avogadro, Count of Quaregna and of Cerreto (1776–1856): Professor of Physics at the University of Turin. His hypothesis that "equal volumes of gases, measured under the same conditions, contain equal numbers of molecules" was proposed in 1811, but its full meaning and significance were not generally realized until 1860 when it was presented again at a scientific congress by Cannizzaro. Avogadro was the first to distinguish between atoms and molecules.

[21] Avogadro's distinction among molecules in general, molecules of elemental substances, and atoms does not follow modern terminology. Because of this, the translation presented may appear inconsistent, but the adjectives which Avodagro used with the word molecule give a clear indication of what he meant if the following definitions are remembered: molecule means either atom or molecule in the modern sense, integral molecules means molecules of compounds (H_2O), constituent molecules means molecules of an elemental substance (H_2 or O_2), elementary molecule means an atom of an elementary substance (H or O).

"Setting out from this hypothesis, it is apparent that we have the means of determining very easily the relative masses of the molecules of substances obtainable in the gaseous state, and the relative number of these molecules in compounds; for the ratios of the masses of the molecules are then the same as those of the densities of the different gases at equal temperature and pressure, and the relative number of molecules in a compound is given at once by the ratio of the volumes of the gases that form it. For example, since the numbers 1.10359 and 0.07321 express the densities of the two gases oxygen and hydrogen compared to that of atmospheric air as unity, and the ratio of the two numbers consequently represents the ratio between the masses of equal volumes of these two gases, it will also represent on our hypothesis the ratio of the masses of their molecules. Thus the mass of the molecule of oxygen will be about 15 times that of the molecule of hydrogen, or, more exactly, as 15.074 to 1. In the same way the mass of the molecule of nitrogen will be to that of hydrogen as 0.96913 to 0.07321, that is, as 13, or more exactly 13.238, to 1. On the other hand, since we know that the ratio of the volumes of hydrogen and oxygen in the formation of water is 2 to 1, it follows that water results from the union of each molecule of oxygen with two molecules of hydrogen. Similarly, according to the proportions by volume established by M. Gay-Lussac for the elements of ammonia, nitrous oxide, nitrous gas, and nitric acid, ammonia will result from the union of one molecule of nitrogen with three of hydrogen, nitrous oxide from one molecule of oxygen with two of nitrogen, nitrous gas from one molecule of nitrogen with one of oxygen, and nitric acid from one of nitrogen with two of oxygen."[22] ▲

By using this reasoning it was possible to assign molecular weights (relative to hydrogen) to all gaseous substances, but the number of atoms in a given molecule of an elementary substance had to be known before relative atomic weights could be calculated. AVOGADRO suggested an answer to this problem.

▼ "There is a consideration which appears at first sight to be opposed to the admission of our hypothesis with respect to compound substances. It seems that a molecule composed of two or more elementary molecules should have its mass equal to the sum of the masses of these molecules; and that in particular, if in a compound one molecule of one substance unites with two or more molecules of another substance, the number of compound molecules should remain the same as the number of molecules of the first substance. Accordingly, on our hypothesis when a gas combines with two or more times its volume of another gas, the resulting compound, if gaseous, must have a volume equal to that of the first of these gases. Now, in general, this is not actually the case. For instance, the volume of water in the gaseous state is,

[22] *Foundations of the Molecular Theory*, pp. 28–31.

as M. Gay-Lussac has shown, twice as great as the volume of oxygen which enters into it, or, what comes to the same thing, equal to that of the hydrogen instead of being equal to that of the oxygen. But a means of explaining facts of this type in conformity with our hypothesis presents itself naturally enough: we suppose, namely, that the constituent molecules of any simple gas whatever are not formed of a solitary elementary molecule, but are made up of a certain number of these molecules united by attraction to form a single one; and further, that when molecules of another substance unite with the former to form a compound molecule, the integral molecule which should result splits up into two or more parts (or integral molecules) composed of half, quarter, etc., the number of elementary molecules going to form the constituent molecule of the first substance, combined with half, quarter, etc., the number of constituent molecules of the second substance that ought to enter into combination with one constituent molecule of the first substance (or, what comes to the same thing, combined with a number equal to this last of half-molecules, quarter-molecules, etc., of the second substance); so that the number of integral molecules of the compound becomes double, quadruple, etc., what it would have been if there had been no splitting-up, and exactly what is necessary to satisfy the volume of the resulting gas."[23]

"Dalton, on arbitrary suppositions as to the most likely relative number of molecules in compounds, has endeavoured to fix ratios between the masses of the molecules of simple substances. Our hypothesis, supposing it well-founded, puts us in a position to confirm or rectify his results from precise data, and, above all, to assign the magnitude of compound molecules according to the volumes of the gaseous compounds, which depend partly on the division of molecules entirely unsuspected by this physicist.

"Thus Dalton supposes that water is formed by the union of hydrogen and oxygen, molecule to molecule. For this, and from the ratio by weight of the two components, it would follow that the mass of the molecule of oxygen would be to that of hydrogen as $7\frac{1}{2}$ to 1 nearly, or, according to Dalton's evaluation, as 6 to 1. This ratio on our hypothesis is, as we saw, twice as great, namely, as 15 to 1. As for the molecule of water, its mass ought to be roughly expressed by $15 + 2 = 17$ (taking for unity that of hydrogen), if there were no division it is reduced to half, $8\frac{1}{2}$, or more exactly 8.537, as may also be found directly by dividing the density of aqueous vapour 0.625 (Gay-Lussac) by the density of hydrogen 0.0732. This mass only differs from 7, that assigned to it by Dalton, by the difference in the values for the composition of water; so that in this respect Dalton's result is approximately correct from the combination of two compensating errors, — the error in the mass of the molecule of oxygen, and his neglect of the division of the molecule."[24]   ▲

_____

[23] *Ibid.*, pp. 31–32.
[24] *Ibid.*, p. 33.

It is a simple matter to convert Avogadro's results to the modern scale of atomic weights. If the relative weight of the hydrogen molecule is taken as unity, the relative weight of the hydrogen atom is 0.5 because Gay-Lussac's results indicated that the hydrogen molecule was diatomic. However, if the *atom* of the lightest element is assigned a weight of unity, the relative molecular weights on the Avogadro scale are doubled. Thus, the relative weight of the hydrogen molecule is 2, and that of the oxygen molecule is 30.[25] Once the distinction between the combining weight of an element (Dalton's "relative atomic weight") and the atomic weight was understood, and the correct formulas for compounds had been deduced by using Avogadro's method, it was only a matter of time before more precise analyses were made which led to more precise values for the atomic weights of the elements.

In summary, the postulates of Dalton's atomic theory as modified by Gay-Lussac and Avogadro are (1) all elements are composed of very small, discrete, indivisible particles called atoms, (2) all atoms of any one element are identical, (3) the atoms of no two elements are alike, and (4) atoms are indestructible bits of matter and are not changed in chemical reactions. In the modern sense, several of these postulates are not true, but the theory provided a stimulus which was to have a profound effect on chemical thought. Thus, a detailed atomic theory based upon experimental facts was established in about a hundred years, whereas the suggestions of Democritus and Aristotle concerning the nature of matter, which were based upon philosophic arguments, had not progressed appreciably in 1900 years. It is at this point in time that the first experiments were performed which would eventually shed light upon the structure of the atom whose existence had just been put on a firm experimental foundation.

SUGGESTED READING

Coward, II. Γ. "John Dalton," *Journal of Chemical Education*, **4**, 23 (1927). A brief survey of Dalton's chemical accomplishments, including some photographs of his original notebook pages.

Ihde, A. J. "Antecedents to the Boyle Concept of the Element," *Journal of Chemical Education*, **33**, 548 (1956).

MacNevin, W. M. "Berzelius — Pioneer Atomic Weight Chemist," *Journal of Chemical Education*, **31**, 207 (1954).

Parravano, N. "Cannizzaro and the Atomic Theory," *Journal of Chemical Education*, **4**, 836 (1927).

Scott, J. H. "The Nineteenth Century Atom: Undivided or Indivisible?" *Journal of Chemical Education*, **36**, 64 (1959).

[25] The difference between Avogadro's value of the molecular weight of oxygen (30) and the modern value (32) is attributable to experimental error.

CHAPTER 2

Electrical Discharge
Through Gases

Although it was not possible to solve the problem of atomic constitution purely by chemical methods, an attempt was made in this direction by William Prout[1] when he suggested that all atoms were composed of integral numbers of hydrogen atoms. This hypothesis was based on the results of early atomic weight determinations which appeared to indicate that the atomic weights of the known elements were integers if hydrogen was taken as unity. As experimental techniques were perfected, it became obvious that the observed atomic weights for some elements were not integers, e.g. chlorine with atomic weight 35.45, and Prout's hypothesis fell into disrepute. We now know that Prout was in a sense correct. The facts that brought about the downfall of Prout's hypothesis, that is, non-integral atomic weights, were misinterpreted because the existence of isotopes was not yet known. The observed atomic weight of an atom corresponds to the average atomic weight of all of the isotopic species in the sample, and, in some cases, this average value may not be near a whole number. In the middle of the nineteenth century the existence of the atom was established, but its constitution was unknown.

CATHODE RAYS

New information concerning the constitution of the atom arose from studies on the conduction of an electric current through gaseous matter at low pressures.

[1] William Prout (1785–1850): An English physician and chemist. Although most of Prout's investigations were in biochemistry or medicinal chemistry, he is most remembered for his hypothesis that the atomic weights of elements are multiples of that of hydrogen. Accurate atomic weight determinations apparently showed this hypothesis to be incorrect, but the modern work on the existence of isotopes indicates that there was a germ of truth in Prout's suggestion.

It was as if nature had anticipated that chemists could do no more with quantitative relationships based on chemical change and had supplied a new area from which to draw important observations. In 1859 Julius Plücker[2] observed that an electric discharge through a highly evacuated tube (pressures less than 10^{-4} cm. of mercury) yields a peculiar type of radiation from the negative electrode (cathode). Twenty years after the discovery of the "cathode rays," Sir William Crookes[3] proposed that they were composed of particles, but it fell to Sir J. J. Thomson[4] to prove that this suggestion was correct.

Cathode rays can be generated quite simply in a highly evacuated tube containing two electrodes (Figure 1). Upon the application of a high potential across these electrodes the glass walls of the tube about the anode (positive electrode) glow with a green light. It might appear that with a good vacuum in the tube no current would flow through the circuit. However, electricity does flow through the external circuit (as indicated by the meter), and the glow at the anode end of the tube persists as long as the circuit is closed. The flow of electricity in the external circuit can only mean that an electric charge is passing through the evacuated tube. In addition to glass, other materials such as zinc sulfide glow brightly when placed in the space between the electrodes. A screen impregnated with zinc sulfide is often used in these experiments, and a solid object placed between the screen and the cathode will cast a shadow on the screen, but no shadow is formed if the object is placed between the screen and the anode. From this simple experiment, it is evident that the rays pass from the cathode to the anode; hence the name "cathode rays."

Although Perrin[5] had shown earlier that cathode rays carry a negative electric

---

[2] Julius Plücker (1801–1868): Professor of Mathematics and later of Physics at the University of Bonn. Early in his career he made notable contributions to the field of analytical geometry, but in 1847 he became interested in experimental physics and investigated the magnetic properties of bodies, the action of a magnet on an electrical discharge, and spectral phenomena. In 1865 Plücker abandoned experimental physics, as readily as he had mathematics earlier, and returned to the study of pure mathematics.

[3] Sir William Crookes (1832–1919): A private scientific investigator whose name is associated with many facets of chemistry. He was founder and editor of *Chemical News*, discoverer of thallium and uranium X, and he also identified helium found in minerals with that found in the sun's spectrum, investigated electric discharges through gases, and invented the spinthariscope.

[4] Sir Joseph John Thomson (1856–1940): Cavendish Professor of Experimental Physics at Cambridge University and Professor of Physics at the Royal Institution. His study of the conduction of electricity through gases led to the discovery and characterization of the electron and the elucidation of the nature of cathode rays as well as to the detection and separation of isotopes. In 1906 he was awarded the Nobel Prize in physics for "recognition of the great services rendered by him in his theoretic and experimental investigations regarding the passage of electricity through gases."

[5] Jean Baptiste Perrin (1870–1942): Professor of Physical Chemistry at the Sorbonne. Although he did work on the nature of the cathode rays early in his career, Perrin is noted for the quantitative confirmation that the Brownian movement is the result of molecular impacts and the determination of Avogadro's number. In 1926 he won the Nobel Prize in physics for this work.

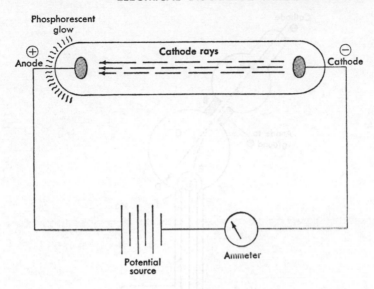

FIGURE 1

A discharge tube of the type used by Plücker to generate cathode rays.
The tube is evacuated and contains two electrodes which are connected to
a source of potential.

charge, J. J. Thomson is generally credited with elucidating the nature of the
cathode rays. Thomson's apparatus which proved that "something charged with
negative electricity is shot off from the cathode, traveling at right angles to it,
and that this something is deflected by a magnet"[6] is illustrated in Figure 2.
The cathode rays were generated at A using an induction coil as a high potential
source. They passed through a metal plug (B) with a slit in it and into the large
evacuated chamber (C). The metal plug was made the anode in this experiment,
and the cathode rays were detected by the phosphorescence they caused when
striking the glass walls at D. By placing the poles of a magnet above and below
the tube the cathode rays could be made to pass through a slit (E) in a grounded
metal shield and through a second slit of a collector electrode (F) that was
connected to an electroscope. The latter is a simple, but sensitive, instrument
which detects the presence of electric charge (see Figure 3, page 17). The lightweight leaf of the electroscope is usually made of gold, and, when an electric
charge is placed on the rigid center strip, the leaf is repelled (Figure 3, B). The
following quotation is THOMSON's description and interpretation of the results
of this experiment.

[6] J. J. Thomson, "Cathode Rays," *Philosophical Magazine*, **44**, 294 (1897).

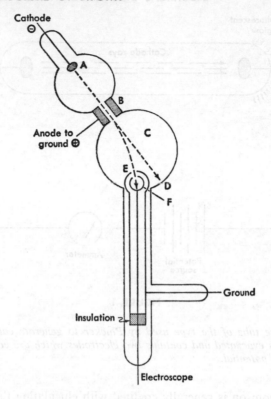

FIGURE 2

The discharge tube by Thomson to investigate the nature of the charge associated with the cathode rays. See the text for a complete description and experimental procedure. Adapted from J. J. Thomson, "Cathode Rays," Philosophical Magazine, 44 (London: Taylor & Francis, Ltd., 1897).

▼   "When cathode rays did not fall on the slit, the electrical charge sent to the electrometer (electroscope) when the induction-coil producing the rays was set in action was small and irregular; when, however, the rays were bent by a magnet so as to fall on the slit there was a large charge of negative electricity sent to the electrometer (electroscope). I was surprised at the magnitude of the charge. If the rays were so much bent by the magnet that they overshot the slits in the cylinder, the charge passing into the cylinder fell to a very small fraction of its value when the aim was true. Thus this experiment shows that however we twist and deflect the cathode rays by magnetic forces, the negative electrification follows the same path as the rays, and that the negative electrification is indissolubly connected with the cathode rays."[7] ▲

[7] *Ibid.,* pp. 294–295.

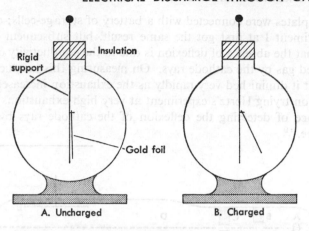

FIGURE 3

An electroscope consists of a lightweight movable metal leaf, usually gold, suspended on a rigid support. (A) When the electroscope is uncharged the movable leaf hangs next to the support; (B) when an electrical charge is conducted to the electroscope the movable leaf is repelled from the support.

The Nature of Cathode Rays

It would appear conclusive from this experiment that cathode rays are negatively charged particles, but other prevalent theories were not easily removed from consideration. Earlier experiments by Hertz[8] attempting to deflect the cathode rays with an electric field were unsuccessful, and Thomson was forced to elucidate this apparent discrepancy. THOMSON'S own words are, perhaps, the best description of the situation which existed and they outline his attack on the problem.

▼ "An objection very generally urged against the view that the cathode rays are negatively electrified particles, is that hitherto no deflexion of the rays has been observed under a small electrostatic force, and though the rays are deflected when they pass near electrodes connected with sources of large differences of potential, such as induction-coils or electrical machines, the deflexion in this case is regarded by the supporters of the aetherial theory as due to the discharge passing between the electrodes, and not primarily to the electrostatic field. Hertz made the rays travel between two parallel plates of metal placed inside the discharge-tube, but found that they were not deflected

[8] Heinrich Hertz (1857–1894): Professor of Physics at Carlsruhe Polytechnic Institute and later at the University of Bonn. Hertz's primary research was in the field of electromagnetic phenomena. He gave experimental proof for the validity of Maxwell's theory in 1887 concerning the relation between light and electricity. In his investigation of the electric discharge he just missed the discovery of X-rays which Röntgen described several years later.

when the plates were connected with a battery of storage-cells; on repeating this experiment I at first got the same result, but subsequent experiments showed that the absence of deflexion is due to the conductivity conferred on the rarefied gas by the cathode rays. On measuring this conductivity it was found that it diminished very rapidly as the exhaustion increased; it seemed then that on trying Hertz's experiment at very high exhaustions there might be a chance of detecting the deflexion of the cathode rays by an electrostatic force."[9]

▲

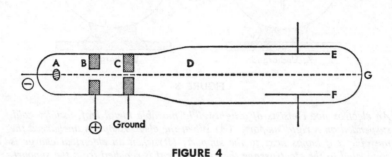

FIGURE 4

The type of discharge tube used by Thomson to show that cathode rays are deflected by an electric field. See the text for a description of the tube. Adapted from J. J. Thomson, "Cathode Rays," Philosophical Magazine, 44 (London: Taylor & Francis, Ltd., 1897).

The apparatus which Thomson used was a modification of Plücker's discharge tube (Figure 1) and is represented in Figure 4. As usual the cathode rays were generated by placing the potential difference from an induction coil across the cathode and the anode (*A* and *B*, respectively). The latter had a slit in it which allowed the rays to enter the larger chamber (*D*). A second narrower slit (*C*) in a metal plug, which was also grounded, defined the cathode rays to a thin beam that passed between two parallel aluminum plates (*E* and *F*) before striking the end of the tube. An arbitrary scale for reference was attached to the surface of the tube (*G*), and the position of the beam was detected by the phosphorescence it produced upon striking the glass. The following is THOMSON'S description of the results of the experiments conducted in this apparatus.

▼   "At high exhaustions the rays were deflected when the two aluminium plates were connected with the terminals of a battery of small storage-cells; the rays were depressed when the upper plate was connected with the negative pole of the battery, the lower with the positive, and raised when the upper

[9] "Cathode Rays," p. 296.

plate was connected with the positive, the lower with the negative pole. The deflexion was proportional to the difference of potential between the plates, and I could detect the deflexion when the potential-difference was as small as two volts. It was only when the vacuum was a good one that the deflexion took place, but that the absence of deflexion is due to the conductivity of the medium is shown by what takes place when the vacuum has just arrived at the stage at which the deflexion begins. At this stage there is a deflexion of the rays when the plates are first connected with the terminals of the battery, but if this connexion is maintained the patch of phosphorescence gradually creeps back to its undeflected position. This is just what would happen if the space between the plates were a conductor, though a very bad one, for then the positive and negative ions between the plates would slowly diffuse, until the positive plate became coated with negative ions, the negative plate with positive ones; thus the electric intensity between the plates would vanish and the cathode rays be free from electrostatic force. Another illustration of this is afforded by what happens when the pressure is low enough to show the deflexion and a large difference of potential, say 200 volts, is established between the plates; under these circumstances there is a large deflexion of the cathode rays, but the medium under the large electromotive force breaks down every now and then and a bright discharge passes between the plates; when this occurs the phosphorescent patch produced by the cathode rays jumps back to its undeflected position."[10]   ▲

In experiments similar to those described above, Thomson showed that the path of the cathode rays (under the same experimental conditions) was independent of the nature of the gas present in the discharge tube. The conclusion concerning the nature of the cathode rays was inescapable and THOMSON'S summary is succinct.

▼   "As the cathode rays carry a charge of negative electricity, are deflected by an electrostatic force as if they were negatively electrified, and are acted on by a magnetic force in just the way in which this force would act on a negatively electrified body moving along the path of these rays, I can see no escape from the conclusion that they are charges of negative electricity carried by particles of matter. The question next arises, What are these particles? are they atoms, or molecules, or matter in a still finer state of subdivision?"[11]   ▲

In an attempt to clarify the nature of the cathode rays Thomson measured the velocity of these particles as well as the value of the ratio of their charge (e) to their mass (m). At the time, it was impossible to calculate either the mass of

[10] *Ibid.*, p. 296.
[11] *Ibid.*, p. 302.

the particles or their charge independently, but, as we shall see, the value of e/m gave conclusive proof that cathode rays were indeed electrons. Two independent methods were used to measure the value of e/m for cathode rays; the first method involves the measurement of the kinetic energy of the cathode rays and the extent to which they are deflected by a magnetic field of known strength and the second involves the effect of both a magnetic field and an electric field. Both methods yielded the velocity of the electrons which comprise the beam.

In the first of these methods the cathode rays are assumed to consist of a stream of N particles per unit time, each particle carrying charge e and having mass m. In any length of time the total quantity of electricity Q which passes in a given length of time is given by Equation 1.

$$Q = Ne \tag{1}$$

If it is assumed that all the particles in the beam are moving with the same velocity v, the kinetic energy of each particle is given by $\frac{1}{2}mv^2$, and the total kinetic energy, W, for the N particles is given by Equation 2.

$$W = \frac{1}{2}Nmv^2 \tag{2}$$

Now, if the cathode beam in question is subjected to a uniform magnetic field H, then the beam will be deflected and the radius of curvature, ρ, is related to the strength of the magnetic field and the characteristics of the particle by Equation 3.

$$\frac{mv}{e} = H\rho \tag{3}$$

Equations 1, 2, and 3 can be combined and rearranged to give Equations 4 and 5.

$$v = \frac{2W}{QH\rho} \tag{4}$$

$$\frac{e}{m} = \frac{2W}{(H\rho)^2 Q} \tag{5}$$

The experiment was conducted with a discharge tube (Figure 5) in which the cathode rays struck a collector electrode connected to a calibrated electroscope which measured the value of Q in a given experiment; the increase in temperature of the electrode was measured with a calibrated thermocouple. It was assumed that the particles which were moving with a certain kinetic energy gave up all their energy to the collector electrode as heat and this was taken as the value for W in a given experiment. Upon application of a magnetic field of known value the cathode beam was deflected to some point, A, on the side of the tube and

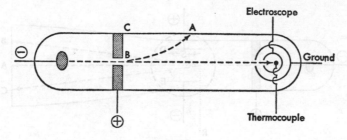

FIGURE 5

The type of discharge tube used by Thomson in his first method to characterize the particles which constitute cathode rays. Using this apparatus Thomson was able to determine the velocity of the "cathode rays" as well as their value of e/m. See the text for a description of the experiment.

the radius of curvature, ρ, could be calculated by simple geometry as

$$2\rho = \frac{(CA)^2}{BC} + BC \tag{6}$$

The experimental procedure was to generate a beam of cathode rays with a given energy (which was governed by the potential applied to the cathode) and allow it to fall on the collector electrode, measuring the total charge collected (Q) and the heat liberated (W); this portion of the experiment was one to two seconds in duration. Then a magnetic field of known strength (H) was applied and the distance CA was measured. Knowing the distance BC, Thomson had all the necessary data to calculate the velocity (Equation 4) of the particles and their e/m values (Equation 5). The velocity of the particles was found to depend upon the magnitude of the potential used to generate the cathode rays and was of the order of 10^9 to 10^{10} centimeters per second. On the other hand, the value of e/m was independent of the nature of the gas in the discharge tube and was about 2×10^{11} coulombs/kilogram.

Thomson's second method for experimentally determining the velocity and the ratio of e/m of the electron consisted of balancing the deflection of a known magnetic field against deflection of a known electric field operating in the opposite direction; a schematic illustration of this method appears in Figure 6. The cathode beam is undeviated when no magnetic or electric field is applied, and a spot appears on the tube face at A. The application of a potential difference between the two plates D and E causes the beam to be deviated upward and the spot appears at some point B, but the beam can be returned to its original position at A by the application of a counter-balancing magnetic field. Using the quantitative relationships which had been proved for the interaction of electric and magnetic fields with moving charges, Thomson showed that under these

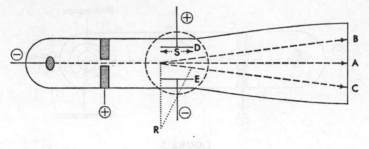

FIGURE 6

The type of discharge tube used in Thomson's second method for characterizing cathode rays. The dotted circle represents the position of the pole faces of a magnet above and below the tube. The magnetic field is perpendicular to the plane of the page.

conditions of balance the velocity of the moving charge, v, was related to the magnetic field, H, and the length of the condenser plates, S, according to Equation 7.

$$v = \frac{V}{HS} \tag{7}$$

Removal of the electric field while maintaining the magnetic field causes the cathode beam to deviate downward, and the phosphorescent spot appears on the tube face at C. Under these conditions e/m is given by the expression

$$\frac{e}{m} = \frac{V}{SH^2R} \tag{8}$$

where R is the radius of curvature of the magnetically deflected cathode beam and can be calculated by simple geometry from the dimensions of the discharge tube and the measured distance CA. The results of this experimental method for the determination of v and e/m were in agreement with those of the first method. A comparison of this value of e/m for cathode rays could now be made with the values obtained for other charged species which were known to exist in aqueous solution.

The electrolysis of solutions of ionic substances had been summarized by Michael Faraday[12] in 1833. It was observed that the mass (m) of a given substance liberated from solution by an electric current is directly proportional to the quantity of electricity (q) passed through the substance. From this observa-

[12] Michael Faraday (1791–1867): The son of a Yorkshire blacksmith who under the patronage of Sir Humphry Davy eventually became Director of the Laboratories at the Royal Institution. His best known researches are on electricity and magnetism, but his chemical investigations were equally fruitful. He formulated the laws of electrolysis, discovered benzene, liquefied chlorine and carbon dioxide, and studied the isomerism of polymeric hydrocarbons.

tion it follows that q/m is constant and experimentally this constant was found to be characteristic of the substance liberated. Some values of q/m as determined experimentally for various ionic species are given in Table 3. By comparing the

TABLE 3
The Charge to Mass Ratio (q/m) for Various Ions

Ion	q/m (coulombs/kilogram)
H^+	9.6×10^7
Cu^{2+}	3.0×10^6
Ag^+	8.9×10^5
Cd^{2+}	1.7×10^6
Fe^{3+}	5.2×10^6

value of e/m (2×10^{11} coulombs/kilogram) for the particles which constitute cathode rays with that of the known ionic species, it is evident that the former are not charged atoms. In addition, the e/m value for cathode rays is about 2000 times larger than that of the lightest known ion, i.e. the hydrogen ion, which indicates that the particle has either a very small mass or an unusually high charge. Since the charges on the majority of chemical ionic species are small multiples of the charge on the hydrogen ion (never approaching ten times that of the hydrogen ion let alone 2000 times), it is reasonable to assume that the difference in values is due primarily to a difference in mass. THOMSON summarized his experimental results as follows:

▼   "Thus on this view we have in the cathode rays matter in a new state, a state in which the subdivision of matter is carried very much further than in the ordinary gaseous state: a state in which all matter — that is, matter derived from different sources such as hydrogen, oxygen, &c. — is of one and the same kind; this matter being the substance from which all the chemical elements are built up."[13]

"The explanation which seems to me to account in the most simple and straightforward manner for the facts is founded on a view of the constitution of the chemical elements which has been favourably entertained by many chemists: this view is that the atoms of the different chemical elements are different aggregations of atoms of the same kind. In the form in which this hypothesis was enunciated by Prout, the atoms of the different elements were hydrogen atoms; in this precise form the hypothesis is not tenable, but if we substitute for hydrogen some unknown primordial substance X, there is nothing known which is inconsistent with this hypothesis...."[14] ▲

[13] "Cathode Rays," p. 312.
[14] *Ibid.*, p. 311.

THOMSON further indicated that the gas molecules in the discharge tube were the source of the cathode rays (electrons).

▼   "If in the very intense electric field in the neighbourhood of the cathode, the molecules of the gas are dissociated and are split up, not into the ordinary chemical atoms, but into these primordial atoms, which we shall for brevity call corpuscles; and if these corpuscles are charged with electricity and projected from the cathode by the electric field, they would behave exactly like the cathode rays. They would evidently give a value of m/e (*sic.*) which is independent of the nature of the gas and its pressure, for the carriers are the same whatever the gas may be; again, the mean free paths of these corpuscles would depend solely upon the density of the medium through which they pass."[15]   ▲

Thus, Thomson suggested that the atom was not indivisible as Dalton had proposed, but consisted, in part, of negatively charged particles which could be removed if sufficient energy were applied to a neutral atom. The cathode rays consist of free electricity and have, moreover, the properties of free negatively charged electrical particles. Many years before Thomson's proof of the existence of a discrete unit of negative electricity C. J. Stoney had given this unit the name of electron. Thomson's investigation into the phenomena of electrical discharge through gases had led to the discovery of the electron and this phenomenon also contained the information which eventually indicated the full complexity of the atom as well as a means for the elucidation of this complexity.

CANAL RAYS

In 1886, E. Goldstein observed a radiation emitted from a perforated cathode but moving in the opposite direction to that of the cathode rays; the design of the discharge tube employed is shown in Figure 7. The cathode, A, consists of a metal plate with a large number of holes drilled in it, the anode is situated at B, the tube is filled with a gas at low pressure, and a high potential is supplied across A and B with an induction coil. Under these conditions the usual cathode rays (C) were observed to stream from A to B and the glass about the anode became phosphorescent. On the other side of the cathode bundles of light (D) appeared to stream from each of the holes in the cathode. The color of these beams varied with the gas in the discharge tube, but Goldstein was unable to observe whether they were affected by a magnetic field. Because the nature of this radiation was unknown and the rays were observed streaming through the holes or channels in the cathode, Goldstein called them "Kanalstrahlen" or canal rays. In 1898, a year after Thomson had published his definitive work on

[15] *Ibid.*

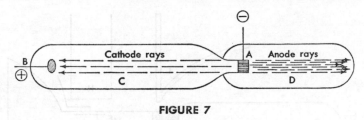

FIGURE 7

*Goldstein modified the usual discharge tube by using a perforated cathode
to show the existence of canal rays (Kanalstrahlen).*

cathode rays, W. Wien[16] showed that the canal rays carried a charge by observing their deflection in a magnetic or electrostatic field. Moreover, the deflection of the canal rays was in the opposite direction to that observed for the deflection of cathode rays. Since the latter had been proved to be negative particles, the canal rays must be a stream of positive particles. Although Wien had shown that the value of e/m for the canal rays with a given gas in the discharge tube was much smaller than those observed for cathode rays by Thomson, it was the latter investigator and his students who ultimately showed the significance of the canal radiation.

Thomson's investigations of the nature of the canal rays, or positive rays, as he called them, essentially used the method that he developed for the elucidation of cathode rays; however, the results were more fruitful in a sense. Wien's experiments concerning the sign of the electrical charge which the canal rays carried were confirmed, and Thomson refined Wien's estimates of e/m for the positive particles using the discharge tube illustrated in Figure 8. The cathode, A, had a fine hole through it along the axis of the tube; the positive rays (B) were emitted in a narrow beam when a high potential source was placed across the cathode and the anode, C. The position of the beam was observed on the flattened end, D, of the discharge tube covered with a uniform layer of willemite; the latter substance is more strongly phosphorescent than glass when struck by canal rays. In later work the location of the canal rays was determined and recorded permanently by allowing them to fall on a photographic plate which became "exposed" at the points where the rays struck. The beam of rays passed between two parallel plates E and F and the poles of an electromagnet G and H and could thus be subjected to electrostatic and/or magnetic fields of known strength. A soft iron shield, I, screened the main part of the discharge tube from the magnetic field. In general, the deflection due to a magnetic field acting on positive rays was only about two percent of the deflection of the same field on the cathode rays.

---

[16] Wilhelm Wien (1864–1928). He is known for his work with cathode rays, canal rays, and light radiation. In 1911 he received the Nobel Prize for "his discoveries regarding the laws governing the radiation of heat."

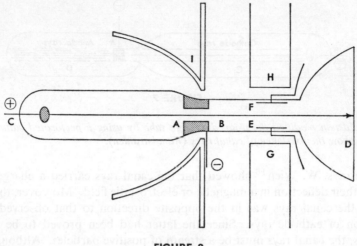

FIGURE 8

Thomson's discharge tube used for the determination of e/m for the particles which constitute canal rays. See the text for a description.

The values of e/m for the particles which make up the canal rays were determined experimentally by measuring the deflection of the beam by known magnetic and electrostatic fields. If it is assumed that a particle of mass m, velocity v, and charge e passes between the poles of a magnet and two electrically charged plates arranged as in Figure 9, the particle experiences a deflection due to each field as indicated. The forces acting on the particle (f_m and f_e) deflect it from the undeviated path, and Thomson showed that the deflection in the X direction is given by

$$X = C_1 \frac{Ee}{mv^2} \qquad (9)$$

where E is the electric field between the plates and C_1 is a constant that depends upon the geometry of the apparatus; the deflection in the Y direction is given by

$$Y = C_2 \frac{He}{mv} \qquad (10)$$

where H is the magnetic field and C_2 is also a constant. Equations 9 and 10 can be combined and rearranged to give

$$\frac{Y}{X} = \frac{C_2 H}{C_1 E} \cdot v \qquad (11)$$

and

$$\frac{Y^2}{X} = \frac{C_2^2 H^2}{C_1 E} \cdot \frac{e}{m} \qquad (12)$$

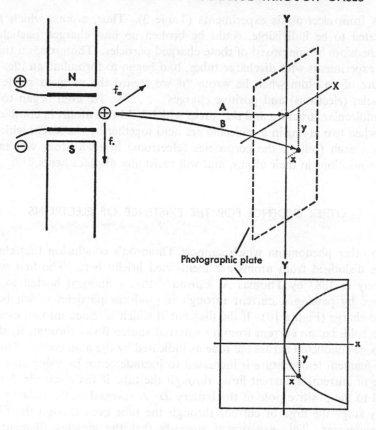

FIGURE 9

Details of the method Thomson used for determining e/m for canal rays using the apparatus shown in Figure 8. (A) represents the undeviated beam and (B) is the position of the beam under the influence of the magnetic and electric fields. Adapted from J. J. Thomson, Rays of Positive Electricity and Their Applications to Chemical Analysis (London: Longmans, Green & Co., Inc., 1913).

Thus the velocity of the particle is proportional to the ratio of the Y deflection to the X deflection for a given experiment, whereas e/m is proportional to Y^2/X. Particles moving with a fixed velocity give a straight line ($X/Y = $ constant) which passes through the intersection of the X-Y axis, and particles for which e/m is constant give a parabola ($Y^2/X = $ constant) which passes through the origin (Figure 9). These curves were recorded on a photographic plate which was put in place of the phosphorescent screen ordinarily used. The experimental values of e/m were dependent on the nature of the gas in the discharge tube, e.g. H_2, He, O_2, and were greater than those observed for the cathode rays but were of the same order as those values obtained for ionic species from electrolysis experiments (Table 3). Thus, atoms, which Dalton postulated to be indivisible, could be broken up into charged particles and must therefore be composed of these charged particles. Thomson, on the basis of his experiments with discharge tubes, had begun to formulate an idea of the structure of an atom when he wrote "if we regard the atom as made up of corpuscles (electrons) and positive charges . . . ."[17] He even began to touch upon molecular structure and the forces which hold two atoms in combination. "For when two atoms in a molecule are held together by the forces which they exert on each (other), the corpuscles (electrons) in each atom will take up definite positions in their atoms, and will resist any displacements."[18]

OTHER EVIDENCE FOR THE EXISTENCE OF ELECTRONS

Two other phenomena which support Thomson's conclusion that electrons can be dislodged from atoms are mentioned briefly here. The first was the discovery in 1883 by Thomas A. Edison[19] that a filament heated to incandescence by passing a current through it produces particles which bear an electric charge (Figure 10). If the filament A which is sealed into an evacuated tube is cold, i.e. no current from an external source flows through it, there is no charge conducted across the tube as indicated by the ammeter C. However, as the filament temperature is increased to incandescence by using an external source of current, a current flows through the tube if the electrode B is connected to the positive pole of the battery D. A reversal of the polarity of the battery stops the flow of current through the tube even though the filament is incandescent. This experiment suggests that the glowing filament emits particles that have a negative charge. The value of e/m for these particles is the same as that observed by Thomson for cathode rays.

The second apparently unrelated phenomenon which supports Thomson's suggestions was the observation by Hertz in 1887 that a spark could be made to leap across a gap more readily if ultraviolet light were allowed to fall on the electrodes. This observation led to a series of experiments by other investigators which soon established that metal surfaces lose electrical charge, i.e. neutral surfaces become positively charged and negatively charged surfaces become less negatively charged when irradiated with light; the ability to lose

---

[17] Sir J. J. Thomson, *Rays of Positive Electricity and Their Applications to Chemical Analysis* (London: Longmans, Green and Company, Inc., 1913), p. 43.

[18] *Ibid.*

[19] Thomas Alva Edison (1847–1931): A "self-made" American scientist, Edison had a native genius for solving mechanical and electrical problems. At the time of his death the United States Patent Office had more than 1200 patents credited to him. The United States Congress awarded him a gold medal for his achievements, and at that time a value of 16 billion dollars was placed on his inventive contributions to   humanity. Perhaps his most important contribution to understanding the structure of atoms was the "Edison effect" — the flow of electrons from hot filaments — observed in his early lamp.

electric charge depends upon the nature of the metal and the wave length of the irradiating light. The more chemically active metals such as the alkali and alkaline earth metals are the most active in this respect. Figure 11 illus-

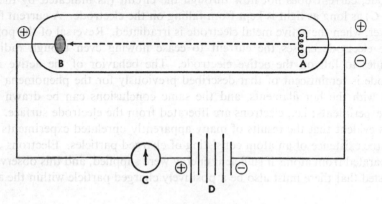

FIGURE 10

The thermoionic effect can be detected with a discharge tube carrying a filament that is heated (A). The electrons that leave the surface are accelerated or repelled from electrode (B) by proper choice of the polarity of (B).

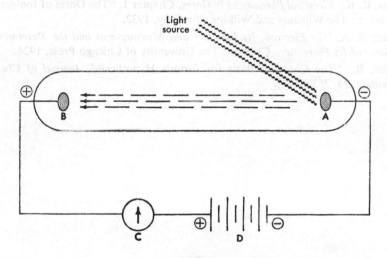

FIGURE 11

A representation of the apparatus which can be used to detect the photoelectric effect. Light of the correct wave length falling on a negatively charged electrode causes electrons to leave the metal surface. This flow of electrons in the tube constitutes a current and is detected as a current flowing in the external circuit.

trates a simple apparatus with which the photoelectric effect may be demonstrated. The electrode A is coated with an active metal, and the tube is evacuated. With the negative pole of the battery D connected to the active metal electrode, current does not flow through the circuit (as indicated by the ammeter C) as long as light is kept from falling on the electrode. A current flows, however, when the active metal electrode is irradiated. Reversal of the polarity of the electrode causes the current to cease flowing even though radiation continues to fall on the active electrode. The behavior of the active metal electrode is reminiscent of that described previously for the phenomena associated with the hot filaments, and the same conclusions can be drawn from these experiments; i.e., electrons are liberated from the electrode surface.

It is evident that the results of many apparently unrelated experiments indicated the existence of an atom consisting of charged particles. Electrons could be separated from atoms if sufficient energy were supplied, and this observation suggested that there must also be a positively charged particle within the atom

SUGGESTED READING

Benfey, O. T. "Prout's Hypothesis," *Journal of Chemical Education*, **29**, 78 (1952).

Darrow, K. K. *Electrical Phenomena in Gases*, Chapter 1, "The Onset of Ionization." Baltimore: The Williams and Wilkins Company, 1932.

Millikan, R. A. *The Electron, Its Isolation and Measurement and the Determination of Some of Its Properties*. Chicago: The University of Chicago Press, 1924.

Siegfried, R. "The Chemical Basis for Prout's Hypothesis," *Journal of Chemical Education*, **33**, 263 (1956).

CHAPTER 3

Isotopes

X-RAYS

The last half of the 19th century was particularly fruitful in producing apparently unrelated discoveries which eventually helped to elucidate atomic structure. So it was with the discovery of X-rays in 1895 by Wilhelm Konrad Röntgen.[1] Most likely, earlier investigators who had employed evacuated discharge tubes in their experiments had produced X-rays unknowingly, but RÖNTGEN's experiments, described in his own words, revealed the existence of the new radiation.

▼ "If the discharge of a fairly large induction-coil be made to pass through a Hittorf vacuum-tube, or through a Lenard tube, a Crookes tube, or other similar apparatus, which has been sufficiently exhausted, the tube being covered with thin, black card-board which fits it with tolerable closeness, and if the whole apparatus be placed in a completely darkened room, there is observed at each discharge a bright illumination of a paper screen covered with barium platino-cyanide, placed in the vicinity of the induction-coil, the fluorescence thus produced being entirely independent of the fact whether the coated or the plain surface is turned towards the discharge-tube. This fluorescence is visible even when the paper screen is at a distance of two metres from the apparatus.

[1] Wilhelm Konrad von Röntgen (1845–1923): Professor of Physics at Strassburg (1876), Giessen (1879), Würzburg (1885), and Munich (1899). Although Röntgen carried out research on light, heat, elasticity, and electricity, none of these investigations approached his discovery of X-rays in importance. X-Rays were discovered while he was experimenting on the conduction of electricity through gases. Although he thought this radiation to be a form of light, the doubt which lingered in his mind prompted him to give it a noncommittal name — X-rays. He received the Nobel Prize in physics in 1901 for "the exceptional services rendered by him in the discovery of the special rays which have been called after him."

"It is easy to prove that the cause of the fluorescence proceeds from the discharge-apparatus, and not from any other point in the conducting circuit.

"The most striking feature of this phenomenon is the fact that an active agent here passes through a black card-board envelope, which is opaque to the visible and the ultra-violet rays of the sun or of the electric arc; an agent, too, which has the power of producing active fluorescence. Hence we may first investigate the question whether other bodies also possess this property.

"We soon discover that all bodies are transparent to this agent, though in very different degrees. I proceed to give a few examples: Paper is very transparent (By 'transparency' of a body I denote the relative brightness of a fluorescent screen placed close behind the body, referred to the brightness which the screen shows under the same circumstances, though without the interposition of the body.); behind a bound book of about one thousand pages I saw the fluorescent screen light up brightly, the printers' ink offering scarcely a noticeable hindrance. In the same way the fluorescence appeared behind a double pack of cards; a single card held between the apparatus and the screen being almost unnoticeable to the eye. A single sheet of tin-foil is also scarcely perceptible; it is only after several layers have been placed over one another that their shadow is distinctly seen on the screen. Thick blocks of wood are also transparent, pine boards two or three centimetres thick absorbing only slightly. A plate of aluminum about fifteen millimetres thick, though it enfeebled the action seriously, did not cause the fluorescence to disappear entirely. Sheets of hard rubber several centimetres thick still permit the rays to pass through them. (For brevity's sake I shall use the expression 'rays'; and to distinguish them from others of this name I shall call them 'X-rays.') Glass plates of equal thickness behave quite differently, according as they contain lead (flint-glass) or not; the former are much less transparent than the latter. If the hand be held between the discharge-tube and the screen, the darker shadow of the bones is seen within the slightly dark shadow-image of the hand itself. Water, carbon disulphide, and various other liquids, when they are examined in mica vessels, seem also to be transparent. That hydrogen is to any considerable degree more transparent than air I have not been able to discover. Behind plates of copper, silver, lead, gold, and platinum the fluorescence may still be recognized, though only if the thickness of the plates is not too great. Platinum of a thickness of 0.2 millimetre is still transparent; the silver and copper plates may even be thicker. Lead of a thickness of 1.5 millimetres is practically opaque; and on account of this property this metal is frequently most useful. A rod of wood with a square cross-section (20 × 20 millimetres), one of whose sides is painted white with lead paint, behaves differently according as to how it is held between the apparatus and the screen. It is almost entirely without action when the X-rays pass through it parallel to the painted side; whereas the stick throws a dark shadow when the rays are made to traverse it perpendicular to the painted side. In a series similar to that of the metals themselves their salts can be arranged with reference to their transparency, either in the solid form or in solution."[2]

"The fluorescence of barium platino-cyanide is not the only recognizable effect of the X-rays. It should be mentioned that other bodies also fluoresce; such, for instance, as the phosphorescent calcium compounds, then uranium glass, ordinary glass, calcite, rock-salt, and so on.

"Of special significance in many respects is the fact that photographic dry plates are sensitive to the X-rays. We are, therefore, in a condition to determine more definitely many phenomena, and so the more easily to avoid deception; wherever it has been possible, therefore, I have controlled, by means of photography, every important observation which I have made with the eye by means of the fluorescent screen.

"In these experiments the property of the rays to pass almost unhindered through thin sheets of wood, paper, and tin-foil is most important. The photographic impressions can be obtained in a non-darkened room with the photographic plates either in the holders or wrapped up in paper. On the other hand, from this property it results as a consequence that undeveloped plates cannot be left for a long time in the neighborhood of the discharge-tube, if they are protected merely by the usual covering of pasteboard and paper.

"It appears questionable, however, whether the chemical action on the silver salts of the photographic plates is directly caused by the X-rays. It is possible that this action proceeds from the fluorescent light which, as noted above, is produced in the glass plate itself or perhaps in the layer of gelatin. 'Films' can be used just as well as glass plates.

"I have not yet been able to prove experimentally that the X-rays are able also to produce a heating action; yet we may well assume that this effect is present, since the capability of the X-rays to be transformed is proved by means of the observed fluorescence phenomena. It is certain, therefore, that all the X-rays which fall upon a substance do not leave it again as such.

"The retina of the eye is not sensitive to these rays. Even if the eye is brought close to the discharge-tube, it observes nothing, although, as experiment has proved, the media contained in the eye must be sufficiently transparent to transmit the rays.

"After I had recognized the transparency of various substances of relatively considerable thickness, I hastened to see how the X-rays behaved on passing through a prism, and to find whether they were thereby deviated or not.

[2] George F. Barker, ed., *Harper's Scientific Memoirs, Röntgen Rays* (New York: Harper and Brothers, 1899), pp. 3–5.

"Experiments with water and with carbon disulphide enclosed in mica prisms of about 30° refracting angle showed no deviation, either with the fluorescent screen or on the photographic plate. For purposes of comparison the deviation of rays of ordinary light under the same conditions was observed; and it was noted that in this case the deviated images fell on the plate about 10 or 20 millimetres distant from the direct image. By means of prisms made of hard rubber and of aluminium, also of about 30° refraction angle, I have obtained images on the photographic plate in which some small deviation may perhaps be recognized. However, the fact is quite uncertain; the deviation, if it does exist, being so small that in any case the refractive index of the X-rays in the substances named cannot be more than 1.05 at the most. With a fluorescent screen I was also unable to observe any deviation.

"Up to the present time experiments with prisms of denser metals have given no definite results, owing to their feeble transparency and the consequently diminished intensity of the transmitted rays.

"With reference to the general conditions here involved on the one hand, and on the other to the importance of the question whether the X-rays can be refracted or not on passing from one medium into another, it is most fortunate that this subject may be investigated in still another way than with the aid of prisms. Finely divided bodies in sufficiently thick layers scatter the incident light and allow only a little of it to pass, owing to reflection and refraction; so that if powders are as transparent to X-rays as the same substances are in mass — equal amounts of material being presupposed — it follows at once that neither refraction nor regular reflection takes place to any sensible degree. Experiments were tried with finely powdered rock-salt, with fine electrolytic silver-powder, and with zinc-dust, such as is used in chemical investigations. In all these cases no difference was detected between the transparency of the powder and that of the substance in mass, either by observation with the fluorescent screen or with the photographic plate.

"From what has now been said it is obvious that the X-rays cannot be concentrated by lenses; neither a large lens of hard rubber nor a glass lens having any influence upon them. The shadow-picture of a round rod is darker in the middle than at the edge; the image of a tube which is filled with a substance more transparent than its own material is lighter at the middle than at the edge.

"The question as to the reflection of the X-rays may be regarded as settled, by the experiments mentioned in the preceding paragraph, in favor of the view that no noticeable regular reflection of the rays takes place from any of the substances examined. Other experiments, which I here omit, lead to the same conclusion.

"One observation in this connection should, however, be mentioned, as at first sight it seems to prove the opposite. I exposed to the X-rays a photographic plate which was protected from the light by black paper, and the glass side of which was turned towards the discharge-tube giving the X-rays. The sensitive film was covered, for the most part, with polished plates of platinum, lead, zinc, and aluminium arranged in the form of a star. On the developed negative it was seen plainly that the darkening under the platinum, the lead, and particularly the zinc, was stronger than under the other plates, the aluminium having exerted no action at all. It appears, therefore, that these three metals reflect the rays. Since, however, other explanations of the stronger darkening are conceivable, in a second experiment, in order to be sure, I placed between the sensitive film and the metal plates a piece of thin aluminium-foil, which is opaque to ultraviolet rays, but is very transparent to the X-rays. Since the same result substantially was again obtained, the reflection of X-rays from the metals above named is proved."[3]

"The justification for calling by the name 'rays' the agent which proceeds from the wall of the discharge-apparatus I derive in part from the entirely regular formation of shadows, which are seen when more or less transparent bodies are brought between the apparatus and the fluorescent screen (or photographic plate).

"I have observed, and in part photographed, many shadow-pictures of this kind, the production of which has a particular charm. I possess, for instance, photographs of the shadow of the profile of a door which separates the rooms in which, on one side, the discharge-apparatus was placed, on the other the photographic plate; the shadow of the bones of the hand; the shadow of a covered wire wrapped on a wooden spool; of a set of weights enclosed in a box; of a galvanometer in which the magnetic needle is entirely enclosed by metal; of a piece of metal whose lack of homogeneity becomes noticeable by means of the X-rays, etc."[4]

THE DISCOVERY OF RADIOACTIVITY

In further experiments Röntgen described the ability of X-rays to cause ionization of gases, which thus become conductors, and showed that this radiation was not deviated by either magnetic or electric fields. X-Rays were eventually proved to be electromagnetic in nature; i.e., they behaved like ordinary visible light. Röntgen's experiments led naturally to speculation concerning the origin

[3] *Ibid.*, pp. 6–9.
[4] *Ibid.*, p. 11.

of X-rays. The French scientist Henri Becquerel[5] suggested that the source of X-radiation lies in the phosphorescence that certain substances exhibited when irradiated by light, and, in attempting to verify this suggestion (which proved to be wrong), he discovered a phenomenon which he called radioactivity. In his investigation into the nature of X-rays, BECQUEREL chose to study, among other substances, a phosphorescent salt of uranium, and a partial description of his experiments and results follows:

▼   "With the double sulphate of uranium and potassium, of which I possess crystals in the form of a thin transparent crust, I have made the following experiment:

"I wrapped a Lumière photographic plate with bromized emulsion with two sheets of thick black paper, so thick that the plate did not become clouded by exposure to the sun for a whole day. I placed on the paper a plate of the phosphorescent substance, and exposed the whole thing to the sun for several hours. When I developed the photographic plate I saw the silhouette of the phosphorescent substance in black on the negative. If I placed between the phosphorescent substance and the paper a coin or a metallic screen pierced with an open-work design, the image of these objects appeared on the negative.

"The same experiments can be tried with a thin sheet of glass placed between the phosphorescent substance and the paper, which excludes the possibility of a chemical action resulting from vapors which might emanate from the substance when heated by the sun's rays.

"We may therefore conclude from these experiments that the phosphorescent substance in question emits radiations which penetrate paper that is opaque to light, and reduce silver salts.

"I particularly insist on the following fact, which appears to me exceedingly important and not in accord with the phenomena which one might expect to observe: the same encrusted crystals placed with respect to the photographic plates in the same conditions and acting through the same screens, but protected from the excitation of incident rays and kept in the dark, still produce the same photographic effects. I may relate how I was led to make this observation: among the preceding experiments some had been made ready on Wednesday the 26th and Thursday the 27th of February and as on those days the sun only showed itself intermittently I kept my arrangements all prepared and put back the holders in the dark in the drawer

[5] Henri Becquerel (1852–1908): Professor of Physics at the Paris École Polytechnique and at the Museum of Natural History in Paris. His primary interest was in the phenomenon of fluorescence and because of this he discovered radioactivity. It was at his suggestion that Madame Marie Sklodowska Curie undertook the chemical examination of pitchblende which eventually led to the discovery of radium. Becquerel received the Nobel Prize in physics in 1903 (shared with the Curies) for "the special services rendered by him in the discovery of spontaneous radioactivity."

of the case, and left in place the crusts of uranium salt. Since the sun did not show itself again for several days I developed the photographic plates on the 1st. of March, expecting to find the images very feeble. The silhouettes appeared on the contrary with great intensity. I at once thought that the action might be able to go on in the dark, and I arranged the following experiment.

"At the bottom of a box made of opaque cardboard, I placed a photographic plate, and then on the sensitive face I laid a crust of uranium salt which was convex, so that it only touched the emulsion at a few points; then alongside of it I placed on the same plate another crust of the same salt, separated from the emulsion by a thin plate of glass; this operation was carried out in the dark room, the box was shut, was then enclosed in another cardboard box, and put away in a drawer.

"I did the same thing with a holder closed by an aluminium plate, in which I put a photographic plate and then laid on it a crust of uranium salt. The whole was enclosed in an opaque box and put in a drawer. After five hours I developed the plates, and the silhouettes of the encrusted crystals showed black, as in the former experiment, and as if they had been rendered phosphorescent by light. In the case of the crust which was placed directly on the emulsion, there was a slightly different action at the points of contact from that under the parts of the crust which were about a millimeter away from the emulsion; the difference may be attributed to the different distances of the sources of the active radiation. The action of the crust placed on the glass plate was very slightly enfeebled, but the form of the crust was very well reproduced. Finally, in passing through the plate of aluminium, the action was considerably enfeebled but nevertheless was very clear.

"It is important to notice that this phenomenon seems not to be attributable to luminous radiation emitted by phosphorescence, since at the end of one hundredth of a second these radiations become so feeble that they are scarcely perceptible.

"Some months ago I showed that uranium salts emit radiations whose existence has not hitherto been recognized, and that these radiations possess remarkable properties, some of which are similar to the properties studied by M. Röntgen. The radiations of uranium salts are emitted not only when the substances are exposed to light but when they are kept in the dark, and for more than two months the same pieces of different salts, kept protected from all known exciting radiations, continued to emit, almost without perceptible enfeeblement, the new radiations. From the 3d. of March to the 3d. of May these substances were enclosed in a box of opaque cardboard. Since the 3d. of May they have been in a double box of lead, which has never left the dark room. A very simple arrangement makes it possible to slip a photographic plate under a black paper stretched parallel to the bottom of the box, on which rests the substances which are being tested, without exposing them to any radiation which does not pass through the lead.

"In these conditions the substances studied continued to emit active radiation.

"All the salts of uranium that I have studied, whether they become phosphorescent or not in the light, whether crystallized, cast or in solution, have given me similar results. I have thus been led to think that the effect is a consequence of the presence of the element uranium in these salts, and that the metal would give more intense effects than its compounds. An experiment made several weeks ago with the powdered uranium of commerce, which has been for a long time in my laboratory, confirmed this expectation; the photographic effect is notably greater than the impression produced by one of the uranium salts, and in particular by the sulphate of uranium and potassium.

"Before publishing this result, I waited until our fellow member, M. Moissan, whose beautiful investigations on uranium have just been published, could put at my disposal some of the products which he had prepared. The results were still sharper and the impressions obtained on the photographic plate through the black paper were much more intense with crystallized uranium, with a casting of uranium, and with uranium carbide than with the double sulphate used as a check on the same plate.

"The same difference appears again in the phenomenon of the discharge of electrified bodies. The metallic uranium provokes the loss of charge at a greater rate than its salts do."[6]   ▲

Becquerel's accidental discovery stimulated great interest in the subject of radioactivity, and in the next few years many significant papers appeared which shed light upon this phenomenon. Two questions became immediately important. What was the substance that emitted the radiation, and what was the nature of the radiation? As we shall see, the answers to both questions provided a clue to the structure of the atom.

Radioactive substances have the ability to cause ionization in gases, and the ions so produced provide a means for electric charge to leak away from the leaves of an electroscope (cf. Chapter 2 and Figure 3). The radiation causing this phenomena was not X-radiation (*vide infra*), but the discharge of an electroscope provided a rapid and quantitative method to follow the course of the radioactive substance through chemical reactions. Investigations into the nature of the radiations emitted from radioactive substances required the use of many techniques including some employed previously by Thomson.

Becquerel had shown that the radiation he observed was characteristic of

[6] HENRI BECQUEREL, "Sur les Radiations Émises par Phosphorescence," *Comptes Rendus*, **122,** 420 (1896), as translated in *A Source Book in Physics*, by William Francis Magee (New York: McGraw-Hill Book Company, Inc., 1935), p. 610.

uranium atoms, and within three years after his original report three new radioactive elements, polonium, radium, and actinium, were discovered by the Curies and Debierne. Previous to this time uranium and thorium were the only elements that were known to be radioactive. A description of the discovery of radium by P. CURIE,[7] M. CURIE,[8] and G. BÉMONT appeared in 1899, and its chemical properties were recorded as follows:

▼ "Two of us have shown that by purely chemical processes we may extract from pitch blende a strongly radioactive substance. This substance stands near bismuth in its chemical properties. We have expressed the opinion that pitch blende perhaps contains a new element, for which we proposed the name polonium.

"The researches which we have since carried on are in agreement with the first results obtained; but in the course of these researches we encountered a second substance also strongly radioactive and entirely different from the first in its chemical properties. In fact, polonium is precipitated in acid solution by sulphuretted hydrogen; its salts are soluble in acids, and water precipitates them from these solutions; polonium is completely precipitated by ammonia.

"The new radioactive substance that we have found presents the chemical aspects of almost pure barium; it is not precipitated either by sulphuretted hydrogen or by ammonium sulphide, or by ammonia; the sulphate is insoluble in water and in acids; the carbonate is insoluble in water; the chloride, very soluble in water, is insoluble in concentrated hydrochloric acid and in alcohol. Finally, it gives the spectrum of barium, which is easy to recognize.

"We believe, nevertheless, that this substance, although for the most part consisting of barium, contains in addition a new element which gives it its radioactivity and which furthermore is very near barium in its chemical properties. These are the reasons which speak in favor of this view.

"(1) Barium and its compounds are not ordinarily radioactive; now, one of us has shown that radioactivity seems to be an atomic property, per-

[7] Pierre Curie (1859–1906): Professor of Physics at the Sorbonne, Paris. Although his initial research was in the phenomenon of piezoelectricity, he is most remembered for the work that was initially done in the field of radioactivity. In 1903, Pierre Curie and his wife received the Nobel Prize in physics (shared with Becquerel) "for the special services rendered by them in the work they jointly carried out in investigating the phenomena of radiation discovered by Professor Henri Becquerel."

[8] Marie Sklodowska Curie (1867–1934): Professor of Physics at the Sorbonne, Paris. The discovery of radioactivity by Becquerel initiated a search for the cause of this phenomenon by Madame Curie. In 1898 she and her husband, Pierre, announced the discovery of the radioactive element polonium (named for her homeland Poland), and in the same year the discovery of radium was announced. In 1903 she shared the Nobel Prize in physics with her husband and Becquerel. Madame Curie was awarded the Nobel Prize in chemistry in 1911 "for her services to the advancement of chemistry by the discovery of the elements radium and polonium, by the isolation of radium and the study of the nature and compounds of this remarkable element."

sisting in all the chemical and physical states of matter. If we look at the thing this way, the radioactivity of our substance, which does not arise from barium, ought to be attributed to another element.

"(2) The first substances which we obtained, in the state of hydrated chlorides, had a radioactivity 60 times greater than that of metallic uranium. (The radioactivity intensity is evaluated by the conductibility of the air in our apparatus.) By dissolving these chlorides in water and precipitating a part of them by alcohol, the precipitated part is much more active than the part which remains dissolved. By starting with this fact we may carry out a series of fractionations, from which we may obtain more and more active chlorides. We have thus obtained chlorides which have an activity 900 times greater than that of uranium. We have been stopped by the lack of material, but from the progress of the operation we may assume that the activity would have been much more increased if we had been able to continue. These facts can be explained by the presence of a radioactive element of which the chloride is less soluble in alcoholic solution than is barium chloride.

"(3) M. Demarçay has examined the spectrum of our substance, with a kindness for which we do not know how to thank him enough. The results of his observations are presented in a special note which follows ours. M. Demarçay has found in the spectrum a band which seems not to belong to any known element. This band, which is scarcely visible in the chloride that is 60 times more active than uranium, becomes strongly marked in the chloride that was enriched by fractionation until its activity was 900 times that of uranium. The intensity of this band increases at the same time as the radioactivity, and this, we think, is a strong reason for attributing it to the radioactive part of our substance.

"The various reasons which we have presented lead us to believe that the new radioactive substance contains a new element, to which we propose to give the name *radium*."[9]   ▲

THE NATURE OF RADIATION EMITTED FROM RADIOACTIVE SUBSTANCES

Further investigation of the radioactivity of uranium, thorium, and radium showed that three types of radiation were continuously and spontaneously emitted, and these were called α-rays, β-rays, and γ-rays. The latter were

[9] P. Curie, M. S. Curie, and M. G. Bémont, "Sur une Nouvelle Substance Fortement Radioactive Contenue dans la Pechblende," *Comptes Rendus*, **127**, 1215 (1898), as translated in *A Source Book in Physics*, by William Francis Magee (New York: McGraw-Hill Book Company, Inc., 1935), pp. 615–616.

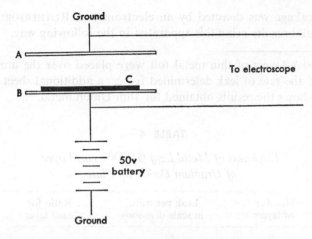

FIGURE 12

Rutherford measured the radioactivity of a substance by measuring its effect on the rate of discharge of a condenser. Plates (A) and (B) are charged with a battery. The rate of discharge of the condenser (as observed with an electroscope) with the radioactive specimen (C) between the plates is a measure of the intensity of radiation emitted by the specimen. Adapted from E. Rutherford, "Uranium Radiation and the Electrical Conduction Produced by It," Philosophical Magazine, 47 (London: Taylor & Francis, Ltd., 1899).

shown to be very similar in character to X-rays. Rutherford[10] proved that α- and β-rays were positively and negatively charged particles, respectively, and hence were not a form of Röntgen's X-rays. The α- and β-rays were characterized by their low penetrating power and by their effect on photographic emulsions.

The complexity of the radiation emitted by radioactive matter was deduced by measuring the leakage of electric charge between two plates of a condenser (Figure 12). Becquerel showed that radioactive substances caused the ionization of gases, and Rutherford used the rate of leakage of electric charge across the plates as a measure of the intensity of the radiation. The radioactive substance under investigation was spread in a thin layer on the lower plate and

[10] Sir Ernest Rutherford, Baron Rutherford of Nelson (1871–1937). Born in New Zealand, pupil of J. J. Thomson, and Professor at McGill University, Montreal (1898), and at the University of Manchester (1907). Rutherford can be considered as the father of the modern atom. His investigations into the disintegration products of radioactive substances, his elucidation of the nature of the α-particle, and the use of this particle as a "probe" to investigate bulk matter led to the concept of a nuclear atom. Rutherford successfully caused the transmutation of atoms of nitrogen, sodium, aluminum, and phosphorus by bombarding them with α-particles. He received the Nobel Prize in chemistry in 1908 "for his investigation into the disintegration of the elements and the chemistry of radioactive substances."

the rate of leakage was detected by an electrometer. RUTHERFORD described his experimental results using this apparatus in the following way.

▼   "Successive layers of thin metal foil were placed over the uranium compound and the rate of leak determined for each additional sheet. The table (Table 4) shows the results obtained for thin Dutch metal.

TABLE 4

Thickness of Metal Leaf 0.00008 cm. Layer of Uranium Oxide on Plate

Number of layers	Leak per min. in scale-divisions	Ratio for each layer
0	91	
		.85
1	77	
		.78
2	60	
		.82
3	49	
		.86
4	42	
		.79
5	33	
		.75
6	24.7	
		.79
8	15.4	
		.77
10	9.1	
		.86
13	5.5	

"In the third column the ratio of the rates of leak for each additional thickness of metal leaf is given. Where two thicknesses were added at once, the square root of the observed ratio is taken, for three thicknesses the cube root. The table shows that for the first ten thicknesses of metal the rate of leak diminished approximately in a geometrical progression as the thickness of the metal increased in arithmetical progression."[11]

"Since the rate of leak diminishes in a geometrical progression with the thickness of metal, we see from the above statement that the intensity of the radiation falls off in a geometrical progression, i.e. according to an ordinary absorption law. This shows that the part of the radiation considered is approximately homogeneous.

"With increase of the number of layers the absorption commences to

[11] E. RUTHERFORD, "Uranium Radiation and the Electrical Conduction Produced by It," *Philosophical Magazine*, **47**, 114 (1899).

diminish. This is shown more clearly by using uranium oxide with layers of thin aluminium leaf. (See Table 5.)

TABLE 5

Thickness of Aluminium Foil 0.0005 *cm.*

Number of layers of aluminium foil	Leak per min. in scale-divisions	Ratio
0	182	
		.42
1	77	
		.43
2	33	
		.44
3	14.6	
		.65
4	9.4	
12	7	

"It will be observed that for the first three layers of aluminium foil the intensity of the radiation falls off according to the ordinary absorption law, and that, after the fourth thickness, the intensity of the radiation is only slightly diminished by adding another eight layers."[12]

"The aluminium foil in this case was about .0005 cm. thick so that after the passage of the radiation through .002 cm. of aluminium the intensity of the radiation is reduced to about $\frac{1}{20}$ of its value. The addition of a thickness of .001 cm. of aluminium has only a small effect in cutting down the rate of leak. The intensity is, however, again reduced to about half of its value after passing through an additional thickness .05 cm., which corresponds to 100 sheets of aluminium foil.

"These experiments show that the uranium radiation is complex, and that there are present at least two distinct types of radiation — one that is very readily absorbed, which will be termed for convenience the α radiation, and the other of a more penetrative character, which will be termed the β radiation.

"The character of the β radiation seems to be independent of the nature of the filter through which it has passed. It was found that radiation of the same intensity and of the same penetrative power was obtained by cutting off the α radiation by thin shields of aluminium foil, tinfoil, or paper. The β radiation passes through all the substances tried with a far greater facility than the α radiation. For example, a plate of thin cover glass placed over the uranium reduced the rate of leak to $\frac{1}{30}$ of its value; the β radiation, however, passed through it with hardly any loss of intensity."[13]

[12] *Ibid.,* p. 115.
[13] *Ibid.,* p. 116.

"It must be remembered that when we are dealing with the β radiation alone, the rate of leak is in general only a few per cent of the leak due to the α radiation, so that the investigation of the homogeneity of the β radiation cannot be carried out with the same accuracy as for the α radiation. As far, however, as the experiments have gone, the results seem to point to the conclusion that the β radiation is approximately homogeneous, although it is possible that other types of radiation of either small intensity or very great penetrating power may be present."[14]

"The photographic actions of the α and β radiations have also been compared. A thin uniform layer of uranium oxide was sprinkled over a glass plate; one half of the plate was covered by a piece of aluminium of sufficient thickness to practically absorb the α radiation. The photographic plate was fixed about 4 mm. from the uranium surface. The plate was exposed 48 hours, and, on developing, it was found that the darkening of the two halves was not greatly different. On the one half of the plate the action was due to the β radiation alone, and on the other due to the α and β radiations together. Except when the photographic plate is close to the uranium surface, the photographic action is due principally to the β radiation."[15] ▲

In addition to the characteristics noted by Rutherford, various other investigators showed that α- and β-rays consist of charged particles. Both of these particles were deflected by a magnetic or electrostatic field, but in opposite directions (Figure 13), and Becquerel determined that the ratio of e/m for β-rays was the same as that obtained by Thomson for cathode rays (electrons). Many radioactive substances emitted γ-rays in addition to α- and β-rays, and these were not deflected in a magnetic or electrostatic field (Figure 13). γ-Rays were later found to be electromagnetic in nature; i.e., they behave like high frequency light rays. Since neither the nature nor the source of γ-rays bears directly upon this discussion of atomic structure, this subject is not considered further.

THE NATURE OF α-PARTICLES

The nature of α-particles was unquestionably established by Rutherford and his collaborators. Previously it had been observed that radium or its com-

[14] *Ibid.*, p. 117.
[15] *Ibid.*, p. 120.

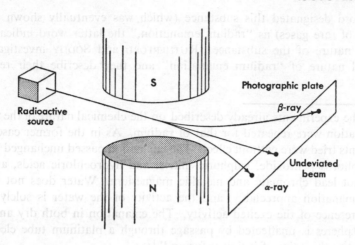

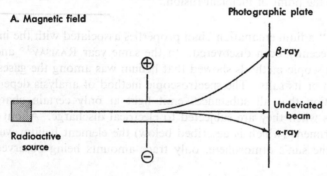

A. Magnetic field

Photographic plate

B. Electrostatic field

FIGURE 13

The α- and β-rays are deflected by a magnetic or electric field because these radiations consist of charged particles. The X-rays are not deflected under these conditions.

pounds emit particles (*vide infra*), and in addition Rutherford and Soddy[16] had shown that a gaseous substance is continuously liberated from this source.

[16] Frederick Soddy (1877–1956): Professor of Chemistry at Aberdeen University and later at Oxford University. The three-year collaboration of Soddy and Rutherford at McGill University resulted in the general theory of radioactive disintegration. Soddy's recognition of isotopic species of elements provided a place in the periodic table for the products of radioactive decay. In 1921 Soddy received the Nobel Prize in chemistry "for his contribution to the chemistry of radioactive substances and his investigations into the origin and nature of isotopes."

Rutherford designated this substance (which was eventually shown to be a mixture of rare gases) as "radium emanation," the latter word indicating the gaseous nature of the substance. RUTHERFORD and SODDY investigated the chemical nature of "radium emanation" and they describe their results as follows:

▼   "The experiments already described on the chemical nature of the thorium emanation were repeated for that of radium. As in the former case all the reagents tried were without effect. The emanation passed unchanged through phosphorus pentoxide, sulphuric, nitric, and hydrochloric acids, and over red hot lead chromate and metallic magnesium. Water does not dissolve the emanation appreciably, and the activity of the water is solely due to the presence of the excited activity. The emanation in both dry and moist atmospheres is unaffected by passage through a platinum tube electrically heated to the point of incipient fusion." [17]   ▲

Thus, the "radium emanation" had properties associated with the inert gases which had recently been discovered. In the same year RAMSAY[18] and SODDY using spectroscopic methods showed that helium was among the gases evolved from radium or its salts. The spectroscopic method of analysis depends upon the observation that all substances emit light at only certain characteristic wave lengths when they are subjected to electrical discharge. About the time of this experiment (which is described below) the element helium was known to exist in the sun's atmosphere, only trace amounts being observed on the earth.

▼   "The gas evolved from twenty milligrams of pure radium bromide [which we are informed had been prepared three months (sic)] by its solution in water and which consisted mainly of hydrogen and oxygen was tested for helium, the hydrogen and oxygen being removed by contact with a red-hot spiral of copper wire, partially oxidized, and the resulting water vapor (removed) by a tube of phosphorus pentoxide. The gas issued into a small vacuum-tube which showed the spectrum of carbon dioxide. The vacuum tube was in train with a small U-tube, and the latter was then cooled with

[17] E. RUTHERFORD and F. SODDY, "The Radioactivity of Polonium and Thorium," *Philosophical Magazine*, **5**, 457 (1903).
[18] Sir William Ramsay (1852–1916): Professor of Chemistry at University College, London. Ramsay's training and his initial research were in the field of organic chemistry, but in 1887 he became interested in other areas of chemistry. This interest eventually led to the discovery of the entire group of rare gases in the air which compose group zero (0) in the periodic table. Argon was discovered in 1894, helium in 1895, neon in 1898, krypton in 1898, and xenon in 1898. In 1904 he received the Nobel Prize in chemistry "for the discovery of gaseous, indifferent elements in the air and the determination of their places in the periodic system."

liquid air. This much reduced the brilliancy of the CO_2 spectrum, and the D_3 line of helium appeared. The coincidence was confirmed by throwing the spectrum of helium into the spectroscope through the comparison prism, and shown to be at least within 0.5 of an Ångstrom unit.

"The experiment was carefully repeated in an apparatus of unused glass with 30 milligrams of radium bromide, probably four or five months old, kindly lent to us by Professor Rutherford. The gases evolved were passed through a cooled U-tube on their way to the vacuum-tube, which completely prevented the passage of carbon dioxide and the emanation. The spectrum of helium was obtained and practically all the lines were seen, including those at 6677, 5876, 5016, 4932, 4713, and 4472. There were also present three lines of approximate wave-lengths 6180, 5695, 5455, that have not yet been identified."[19] ▲

The fact that the gases evolved from radium could be separated into two components, one ("radium emanation") condensing in a trap cooled by liquid air while the other (helium) passed through the trap, led to an investigation of the less volatile "radium emanation." RAMSAY and SODDY showed that "radium emanation" itself slowly formed helium. This experiment is described in their words as follows:

▼ "The maximum amount of the emanation obtained from 50 milligrams of radium bromide was conveyed by means of oxygen into a U-tube cooled in liquid air, and the latter was then extracted by the pump. It was then washed out with a little fresh oxygen which was again pumped off. The vacuum tube sealed onto the U-tube, after removing the liquid air showed no trace of helium. The spectrum was apparently a new one, probably that of the emanation, but this has not been completely examined, and we hope to publish details shortly. After standing from the 17th to the 21st inst. the helium spectrum appeared, and the characteristic lines were observed identical in position with those of a helium tube thrown into the field of vision at the same time. On the 22nd the yellow, the green, the two blue and the violet were seen, and in addition the three new lines also present in the helium obtained from radium. A confirmatory experiment gave identical results."[20] ▲

Rutherford measured the value of e/m for α-particles using the deflection method and came to the conclusion that the mass of the particle was of the same order as that of the hydrogen atom and very large in comparison to the

[19] WILLIAM RAMSAY and FREDERICK SODDY, "Experiments in Radioactivity and the Production of Helium from Radium," *Proceedings of the Royal Society*, 72, 206–207 (1903).
[20] *Ibid.*, p. 207.

mass of a β-ray (electron). The characteristic properties of the α-particle were determined by RUTHERFORD and HANS GEIGER[21] in a deceptively simple experiment which is described in their words as follows:

▼ "In the previous paper, we have determined the number of α-particles expelled per second per gramme of radium by a direct counting method. Knowing this number, the charge carried by each particle can be determined by measuring the total charge carried by the α-particles expelled per second from a known quantity of radium. (Note: Using radium C as a source of α-rays the total number of α-particles expelled per second from one gramme of radium has been accurately counted. For radium in equilibrium, this number is 3.4×10^{10} for radium itself and for each of its three α-ray products. The number of scintillations observed on a properly-prepared screen of zinc sulfide is, within the limit of experimental error, equal to the number of α-particles falling on it.) Since Radium C was used as a source of radiation in the counting experiments, it was thought desirable to determine directly the charge carried by the α-particles expelled from this substance.

"The experimental arrangement is clearly seen in Figure 14. A cylindrical glass tube HH of diameter 4 cm. is closed at the ends by ground-glass stoppers D, E. The source of radiation R is attached to the lower stopper E. The radiation from this passes into the testing chamber, which is rigidly attached to the stopper D by means of an ebonite tube F. The testing chamber consists of two parallel plates A and B about 2 mm. apart. A circular opening, 1.92 cm. in diameter, cut in the brass plate B, is covered by a sheet of thin aluminium foil. The upper chamber AC consists of a shallow brass vessel of aperture 2.5 cm., the lower surface of which is covered also with a sheet of aluminium foil. The plate B is connected through a side glass tube to one terminal of a battery, the other pole of which is earthed. The chamber AC, which is insulated from the plate B, is connected with one pair of quadrants of a Dolezalek electrometer, the other of which is earthed. The whole apparatus is placed between the poles NS of a large electromagnet marked by the dotted lines in the figure, so that the α-rays in their passage from the source R to the testing chamber pass through a strong magnetic field. A very low vacuum is required in these experiments in order to reduce the ionization of the residual gas by the α-rays to as low a value as possible."[22]

"In the present experiments the magnetic field served also for another purpose. Radium C emits β- as well as α-rays, and, in the absence of a

[21] Hans Geiger (1882–1945): Professor of Physics at the Universities of Kiel and Tübingen. He is primarily known for his work on the scattering of radioactive "rays" and for developing instruments to detect these "rays."

[22] E. RUTHERFORD and HANS GEIGER, "The Charge and Nature of the α-Particle," *Proceedings of the Royal Society*, **81,** 162 (1908).

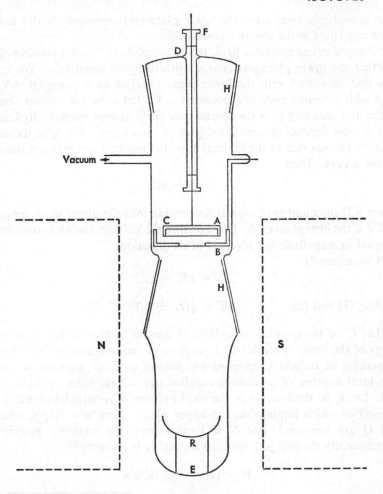

FIGURE 14

Apparatus for the Rutherford-Geiger method for determining the nature of the α-particle. See the text for a description of the experimental procedure. Adapted from E. Rutherford and H. Geiger, "The Charge and Nature of the α-Particle," Proceedings of the Royal Society, 81 (London: The Royal Society, 1908).

magnetic field, these also would be partially absorbed, and give up their negative charges to the upper plate. In the experimental arrangement the magnetic field extended from the source R beyond the testing chamber. The source of radiation was placed about 3.5 cm. below the testing chamber. The strength of the magnetic field was then adjusted, so the β-particles were bent completely away from the lower plate and consequently did not produce any effect in the testing chamber."[23]

"Using a strong magnetic field, the upper plate received a positive charge, whether the lower plate was charged positively or negatively. The current was first measured with the lower plate charged to a potential $+V$, and then with the same plate at a potential $-V$. Let i_1 be the current observed in the first case and i_2 in the second case; i_2 is always numerically less than i_1, the ratio depending upon the degree of exhaustion. Let i_0 be the current through the gas due to the ionization of the residual gas between the plates by the α-rays. Then

$$i_1 = i_0 + nE \tag{1}$$

where n is the number of α-particles passing into the upper plate per second and E is the charge on each. On reversing the voltage, the ionization current is equal in magnitude but reversed in its direction."[24]

"Consequently

$$i_2 = nE - i_0 \tag{2}$$

Adding (1) and (2), $\qquad nE = \frac{1}{2}(i_1 + i_2)$

"Let Q be the quantity of radium C present at any instant measured in terms of the γ-ray effect due to 1 gramme of radium, and N the number of α-particles of radium C expelled per second and per gramme of radium. The total number of α-particles expelled per second from the source R is QN. Let K be the fraction of the total number of α-particles expelled from the source which impinge on the upper plate. Then $n = KQN$, where K and Q are measured, and N is known from the counting experiments. Consequently the charge E on each α-particle is given by[25]

$$E = (i_1 + i_2)/2KQN \qquad \blacktriangle$$

The mean value of many measurements gave a charge of 9.3×10^{-10} E.S.U. for the charge carried by an α-particle from radium C. RUTHERFORD and GEIGER then proceeded to show that the α-particle carries a charge twice the electronic charge.

$\blacktriangledown$ "We shall first of all calculate that the charge E carried by an α-particle on the assumption that the heating effect of radium is a measure of the kinetic energy of the α-particles expelled from it. There is considerable indirect evidence in support of this assumption, for it is known that the

[23] *Ibid.*, p. 164.
[24] *Ibid.*, p. 165.
[25] *Ibid.*, p. 166.

heating effect of the β- and γ-rays together is not more than a few per cent. of that due to the α-rays. If m be the mass of an α-particle and u its initial velocity of projection, the kinetic energy of the α-particle

$$= \frac{1}{2} mu^2 = \frac{1}{2} \frac{mu^2}{E} \cdot E$$

"Now in a previous paper, one of us has accurately determined, from the electrostatic deflection of the α-rays, the values of $\frac{1}{2} \frac{mu^2}{E} \cdot E$ for each of the four sets of α-particles expelled from radium in equilibrium, and has shown that the kinetic energy of the α-particles from 1 gramme of radium in equilibrium is 4.15×10^4 NE ergs, where N is the number of radium atoms breaking up per second.

"Now the heating effect of the standard preparation of radium was 110 gramme-calories per gramme per hour. This is mechanically equivalent to 1.28×10^6 ergs per second. Equating the kinetic energy of the α-particle to the observed heating effect,

$$4.15 \times 10^5 \text{ NE} = 1.28 \times 10^6$$

Substituting the known value $N = 3.4 \times 10^{10}$,

$$E = 9.1 \times 10^{-10} \text{ E.S. unit.}$$

"The agreement of the calculated with the observed value is somewhat closer than one would expect, taking into consideration the uncertainty of the data within narrow limits."[26]

"We have found, experimentally, that the α-particle carries a positive charge E of 9.3×10^{-10} units. If the α-particle has a charge equal to $2e$, the value of e, the charge on the hydrogen atom, becomes 4.65×10^{-10}.

"The value of E/M — the ratio of the charge on the α-particle to its mass — has been measured by observing the deflection of the α-particle in a magnetic and in an electric field, and is equal to 5.07×10^3 on the electromagnetic system. The corresponding value of e/m for the hydrogen atom set free in the electrolysis of water is 9.63×10^3. We have already seen that the evidence is strongly in favour of the view that E = $2e$. Consequently M = $3.84m$, i.e., the atomic weight of an α-particle is 3.84. The atomic weight of helium is 3.96. Taking into account probable experimental errors in the estimates of the value of E/M for the α-particle, we may conclude that *an α-particle is a helium atom*, or, to be more precise, the *α-particle, after it has lost its positive charge, is a helium atom*."[27]   ▲

---

[26] *Ibid.*, p. 168.
[27] *Ibid.*, p. 170.

At this time many other pieces of experimental evidence strongly suggested that the α-particle and a helium atom carrying two positive charges were one and the same, but the critical experiment was performed by RUTHERFORD and ROYDS and is described below.

▼   "We have recently made experiments to test whether helium appears in a vessel into which the α particles have been fired, the active matter itself being enclosed in a vessel sufficiently thin to allow the α particles to escape, but impervious to the passage of helium or other radioactive products."[28]

"The experimental arrangement is clearly seen in the figure (Figure 15). The equilibrium quantity of emanation from about 140 milligrams of radium was purified and compressed by means of a mercury-column into a fine glass tube A about 1.5 cms. long. This fine tube, which was sealed on a larger capillary tube B, was sufficiently thin to allow the α particles from the emanation and its products to escape, but sufficiently strong to withstand atmospheric pressure. After some trials, Mr. Baumbach succeeded in blowing such fine tubes very uniform in thickness. The thickness of the wall of the tube employed in most of the experiments was less than $\frac{1}{100}$ mm., and was equivalent in stopping power of the α particle to about 2 cms. of air. Since the ranges of the α particles from the emanation and its products radium A and radium C are 4.3, 4.8, and 7 cms. respectively, it is seen that the great majority of the α particles expelled by the active matter escape through the walls of the tube. The ranges of the α particles after passing through the glass were determined with the aid of a zinc-sulphide screen."[29]

"The glass tube A was surrounded by a cylindrical glass tube T, 7.5 cms. long and 1.5 cms. diameter, by means of a ground-glass joint C. A small vacuum-tube V was attached to the upper end of T. The outer glass tube T was exhausted by a pump through a stopcock D, and the exhaustion completed with the aid of the charcoal tube F cooled by liquid air. By means of a mercury-column H attached to a reservoir, mercury was forced into the tube T until it reached the bottom of the tube A.

"Part of the α particles which escaped through the walls of the fine tube were stopped by the outer glass tube and part by the mercury surface. If the α particle is a helium atom, helium should gradually diffuse from the glass and mercury into the exhausted space, and its presence could then be detected spectroscopically by raising the mercury and compressing the gases into the vacuum-tube.

"In order to avoid any possible contamination of the apparatus with helium, freshly distilled mercury and entirely new glass apparatus were used. Before introducing the emanation into A, the absence of helium was

[28] E. RUTHERFORD and T. ROYDS, "The Nature of the α Particle from Radioactive Substances," *Philosophical Magazine*, **17**, 281 (1909).
[29] *Ibid.*, pp. 282–283.

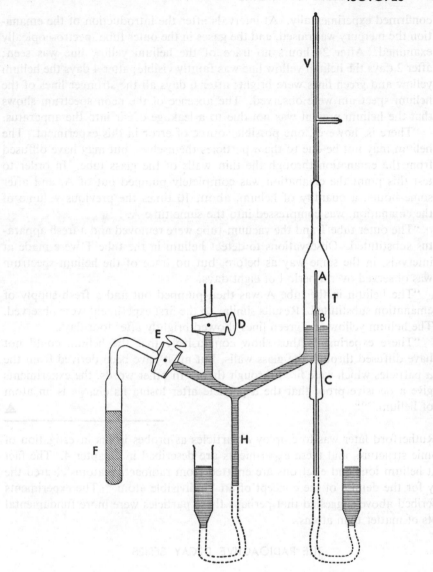

FIGURE 15

The apparatus used by Rutherford and Royds to show that α-particles are ionized helium atoms. See the text for a description of the experiment. Adapted from E. Rutherford and T. Royds, "The Nature of the α-particle from Radioactive Substances," Philosophical Magazine, 17 (London: Taylor & Francis, Ltd., 1909).

confirmed experimentally. At intervals after the introduction of the emanation the mercury was raised, and the gases in the outer tube spectroscopically examined. After 24 hours no trace of the helium yellow line was seen; after 2 days the helium yellow line was faintly visible; after 4 days the helium yellow and green lines were bright; after 6 days all the stronger lines of the helium spectrum were observed. The absence of the neon spectrum shows that the helium present was not due to a leakage of air into the apparatus.

"There is, however, one possible source of error in this experiment. The helium may not be due to the α particles themselves, but may have diffused from the emanation through the thin walls of the glass tube. In order to test this point the emanation was completely pumped out of A, and after some hours, a quantity of helium, about 10 times the previous volume of the emanation, was compressed into the same tube A.

"The outer tube T and the vacuum-tube were removed and a fresh apparatus substituted. Observations to detect helium in the tube T were made at intervals, in the same way as before, but no trace of the helium spectrum was observed over a period of eight days.

"The helium in the tube A was then pumped out and a fresh supply of emanation substituted. Results similar to the first experiment were observed. The helium yellow and green lines showed brightly after four days.

"These experiments thus show conclusively that the helium could not have diffused through the glass walls, but must have been derived from the α particles which were fired through them. In other words, the experiments give a decisive proof that the α particle after losing its charge is an atom of helium."[30]   ▲
_____

Rutherford later was to employ α-particles as probes in his investigation of atomic structure, and these experiments are described in Chapter 4. The fact that helium ions and electrons are emitted from radioactive atoms cleared the way for the demise of the concept of an "indivisible atom." The experiments described above suggested that perhaps these particles were more fundamental units of matter than atoms.

THE RADIOACTIVE DECAY SERIES

The results of intensive activity by many investigators indicated that the radioactive elements uranium, thorium, and actinium gave rise to a great number of other radioactive substances, either directly or indirectly, with an accompanying characteristic radiation. This bewildering array of substances is listed in Table 6, and no attempt is made to present all the data which were used to construct this table.

[30] *Ibid.*, p. 283.

TABLE 6

Radioactive Decay Series[1]

Uranium-radium series	Actinium series	Thorium series
^{238}Uranium$_1$ *	^{231}Uranium Y ⁰	^{232}Thorium ⁰
↓α	↓β	↓α
^{234}Uranium X$_1$ ⁰	^{231}Protoactinium +	^{228}Mesothorium$_1$ **
↓β	↓α	↓β
^{234}Uranium X$_2$ +	^{227}Actinium #	^{228}Mesothorium$_2$ #
↓β	↓β	↓β
^{234}Uranium$_2$ *	^{227}Radioactinium ⁰	^{228}Radiothorium ⁰
↓α	↓α	↓α
^{230}Ionium ⁰	^{223}Actinium X **	^{224}Thorium X **
↓α	↓α	↓α
^{226}Radium **	^{219}Actinium emanation (Radon)	^{220}Thorium emanation (Radon)
↓α	↓α	↓α
^{222}Radium emanation (Radon)	^{215}Actinium A ++	^{216}Thorium A ++
↓α	↓α	↓α
^{218}Radium A ++	^{211}Actinium B zz	^{212}Thorium B zz
↓α	↓β	↓β
^{214}Radium B **	^{211}Actinium C ⁰⁰ (α / β)	^{212}Thorium C ⁰⁰ (α / β)
↓β	^{207}Actinium C'' ^{211}Actinium C' ++	^{208}Thorium C'' ^{212}Thorium C' ++
^{214}Radium C ⁰⁰ (α / β)	(β / α)	(β / α)
^{210}Radium C'' ^{214}Radium C' +	^{207}Actinium C zz	^{208}Thorium D zz
(β / α)		
^{210}Radium D zz		
↓β		
^{210}Radium E ⁰⁰		
↓β		
^{210}Radium F ++		
↓α		
^{206}Radium G zz		

[1] The superscripts refer to the "atomic weight" of the substance. Substances with the same symbols (e.g. *, ⁰, +) have the same chemical properties.

The members of each series were generally characterized by the radiation which they emitted, and the relationship between the members of the series is such that any member is obtained from the member before it and then gives rise to the member following it. This relationship has been given the "daughter-parent" designation. Thus in the uranium-radium series, radium is the daughter element of ionium but the parent of radon. All of the end members of the series are stable; i.e., they are not radioactive. Several interesting chemical observations were made on some of the members of these series. For example, Boltwood[31] showed that ionium was chemically inseparable from thorium and the two substances differed only in their radioactive properties. In 1907 McCoy and Ross showed that thorium and radiothorium (a disintegration product of thorium) were chemically inseparable, and the results of these extensive experiments are concisely summarized by them in the statements at the top of the following page.

[31] Bertram Borden Boltwood (1870–1927): Professor of Chemistry and Physics at Yale University. In 1907 he discovered ionium, the parent element of radium; Hahn and Marckwald also discovered this element independently about the same time.

▼   "But, in spite of the apparently promising results of the preliminary experiments, we did not succeed in separating radiothorium completely from thorium. In fact, it now appears doubtful whether it is possible by chemical treatment to separate any radiothorium from thorium."[32]   ▲

Soddy showed that thorium X, mesothorium, and radium could not be separated by chemical means, and FLECK[33] summarized an extensive investigation of the chemistry of several radioactive substances as follows:

▼   "It has been shown that uranium X and radioactinium are chemically similar to, and non-separable from thorium; mesothorium-2 is non-separable from actinium; thorium-B is non-separable from lead; radium-B and actinium-B are extremely similar to lead, and most probably non-separable from it; thorium-C, radium-C, and actinium-C are very closely allied to bismuth, and probably chemically similar to it. The present view that there is only one product, namely radium-E, between radio-lead and polonium, has been confirmed by the direct measurement of the growth of radium-F from radium-E; finally, radium-E has been shown to possess chemical properties identical with those of bismuth in all respects."[34]   ▲

The question of the fundamental relation between the elements in the radioactive series was confusing to say the least, for there were elements with different atomic weights that had the same chemical properties (e.g., ionium and thorium) whereas others had the same atomic weights (e.g., radium D and radium F) but different chemical properties. SODDY, in his report for the year 1910 on the research completed by many workers in the field of radioactivity, summed up the situation succinctly.

▼   "These regularities may prove to be the beginning of some embracing generalization, which will throw light, not only on radioactive processes, but on elements in general and the Periodic Law. The recognition that elements of different atomic weights may possess identical properties seems destined to have its most important application in the region of inactive elements, where the absence of a second radioactive nature makes it impos-

[32] H. N. McCoy and W. H. Ross, "The Specific Radioactivity of Thorium and the Variation of the Activity with Chemical Treatment and with Time," *Journal of the American Chemical Society*, **29**, 1711 (1907).

[33] Sir Alexander Fleck (1889–   ): At present Chairman of Imperial Chemical Industries in England and President of The Society of Chemical Industry. His early work on the chemistry of radioactive isotopes helped establish the radioactive decay schemes and provided the information for Soddy's explanation of these transformations.

[34] A. FLECK, "The Chemical Nature of Some Radioactive Disintegration Products," *Journal of the Chemical Society*, **103**, 398 (1913).

sible for chemical identity to be individually detected. Chemical homogeneity is no longer a guarantee that any supposed element is not a mixture of several different atomic weights, or that any atomic weight is not merely a mean number. The consistency of atomic weight, whatever the source of the material, is not a complete proof of homogeneity, for, as in the radio-elements, genetic relationships might have resulted in an initial consistency of proportion between the several individuals, which no subsequent natural or artificial chemical process would be able to disturb. If this is the case, the absence of simple numerical relationships between the atomic weights becomes a matter of course rather than one of surprise."[35]   ▲

RUSSELL[36] and ROSSI compared the spark spectrum of pure thorium and that of a mixture of thorium and ionium that was known to contain a large amount of the latter. No new lines were observed with the sample containing ionium. Moreover, the spectra of the two samples were identical. These investigators discussed their results in the following manner.

▼   "There are, however, two other possible ways of explaining our failure to obtain a distinct spectrum for ionium, besides the one discussed above. It is possible that: —

"(1) Ionium has no arc spectrum in the region investigated, or

"(2) Ionium and thorium have identical spectra in the region investigated.

"The first possibility is highly improbable, for all solids of high atomic weights have arc spectra, and, further, all rare earths have highly complicated spectra.

"The second possibility, though somewhat speculative in nature, is suggested by some recent work on the chemical properties of the radio-elements. It is well known that there are no less than four sets of long-lived radio-elements, the members of each of which are chemically non-separable. These elements do not all belong to the group of rare earths, many non-radioactive members of which are known to be chemically very similar. Mesothorium, for instance, which is chemically non-separable from radium, belongs to the alkaline earth group. Again the two non-separable α ray products which are present in ordinary uranium, and which have been called by Geiger and Nuttall uranium I and uranium II belong to the chromium-molybdenum-tungsten group of elements. The explanation of these striking chemical similarities is very probably that the two very similar bodies are really different members of the same group of elements, the

[35] *Chemical Society Annual Reports*, **VII**, 285–286 (1910).
[36] Alexander Smith Russell (1868–   ): Lecturer in Inorganic Chemistry at Oxford University. He carried out chemical research, especially in radioactivity, in Glasgow with Soddy, in Berlin with Nernst, and in Manchester with Rutherford.

difference in their chemical properties being less pronounced than the difference between other members of the same group, owing to the small difference in their atomic weights. *But the possibility that they are identical in all physical and chemical properties, and differ only in atomic weight and in radioactive properties, should not be lost sight of. If this explanation should eventually prove justified, the spectrum of ionium would be identical with that of thorium.*[37]   ▲

THE RECOGNITION OF ISOTOPES

As is often the case in an active field of research, the key to this confusing situation was supplied by several persons at about the same time, each working independently. Russell, Fajans,[38] and Soddy presented the relationship of the known radioactive substances to the periodic classification of the elements. RUSSELL summarized the known data (for example, those data appearing in Table 6) in three tables (Tables 7, 8, and 9) which make the relationship unmistakably clear, and from these tables he derived the following rules which deal with the radioelements.

▼   "1. Whenever an α-particle is expelled by a radio-element the group in the periodic system, to which the resultant product belongs, is either two units greater, or two units less, than that to which the parent body belongs.

"2. Whenever a β-particle or no particle is expelled, with or without the accompaniment of a γ-ray, the group in the periodic system to which the resultant product belongs is one unit greater, or one unit less, than that to which the parent belongs.

"The validity of these two rules is tested in Tables 7, 8, and 9. In Column A of each table is given the name of the radio-element. In Column B is given the common element to which the radio-element is most akin in chemical properties; in C is given the number of the group in the periodic system to which the element in B belongs. The nomenclature is that used in the ordinary arrangement of the elements in the periodic system. . . . In Column E is given the nature of the radiation expelled by the first of any two successive products, in D the actual difference in the group number of the two, and in F the difference in the group numbers of the two which ought to exist if the rules given above are strictly obeyed.

"In Table 10 I have arranged the radio-elements in their places in the

---

[37] A. S. RUSSELL and R. ROSSI, "An Investigation of the Spectrum of Ionium," *Proceedings of the Royal Society*, **87**, 483 (1912).

[38] Kasimir Fajans (1887–   ): His interests are varied and have ranged from radioactivity and isotopes to the structure of glass. In 1913 he and O. H. Göhring discovered uranium X_2, a very short lived isotope of protoactinium. Fajans left Nazi Germany in 1935 where he was Professor of Chemistry at the University of Munich and came to the University of Michigan where he is Professor Emeritus of Chemistry.

TABLE 7—Thorium Series

A Radio-element	B Common element to which this is chemically most akin	C Group in Periodic System to which this element belongs	D Difference in group number of any two successive products	E Radiation expelled	F Calculated difference in group number of any two successive products
Thorium	Thorium	IV.A			
			2	α	2
Mesothorium 1	Radium	II.A			
			1	Rayless	1
Mesothorium 2	Lanthanum	III.A			
			1	β	1
Radio-thorium	Thorium	IV.A			
			2	α	2
Thorium X	Radium	II.A			
			2	α	2
Thorium emanation	Xenon	0			
			4	2α	4
Thorium A	?				
Thorium B	Lead	IV.A			
			1	β	1
Thorium C	Bismuth	IV.A			
			1	α + β	1 or 3
Thorium C	Lead (?)	IV.A			

TABLE 8—Actinium Series

A Radio-element	B Common element to which this is chemically most akin	C Group in Periodic System to which this element belongs	D Difference in group number of any two successive products	E Radiation expelled	F Calculated difference in group number of any two successive products
Actinium	Lanthanum	III.A			
			1	Rayless	1
Radio-actinium 1	Thorium	IV.A			
			2	Rayless α + β	0, 2, or 4
Radio-actinium 2	?				
Actinium X	Radium	II.A			
			2	α	2
Actinium emanation	Xenon	0			
			4	2α	4
Actinium A	?				
Actinium B	Lead	IV.B			
			1	β	1
Actinium C	Bismuth	V.B			
			1	α + β	1 or 3
Actinium D	Lead (?)	IV.B			

TABLE 9—*Uranium Series*

A Radio-element	B Common element to which this is chemically most akin	C Group in Periodic System to which this element belongs	D Difference in group number of any two successive products	E Radiation expelled	F Calculated difference in group number of any two successive products
Uranium I	Uranium	VI.A	2	α	2
Uranium X_1 Uranium X_2	Thorium ?	IV.A	2	Rayless (?) β	0 or 2
Uranium 2	Uranium	VI.A	2	α	2
Ionium	Thorium	IV.A	2	α	2
Radium	Radium	II.A	2	α	2
Radium emanation Radium A	Xenon ?	0	4	2α	4
Radium B	Lead	IV.B	1	β	1
Radium C	Bismuth	V.B	1	$\beta + \alpha$	1 or 3
Radium D	Lead	IV.B	1	β	1
Radium E	Bismuth	V.B	1	β	1
Radium F	Tellurium	VI.B	2	α	2
Radium G (Lead)	Lead	IV.B			

periodic system. In the top line of the table, the groups of the periodic system are arranged in descending order from VI.A to O, and in ascending order from O to VI.B. Under the name of each group is put the name of the common element of highest atomic weight belonging to that group. Under each of these elements are placed the radio-elements which are either chemically non-separable, or chemically most akin to it. I have placed uranium X and radio-actinium 2 in group V.A, though at present the existence of the first, and the exact chemical nature of the second, is not yet known. These are the places in the periodic system that these elements should occupy if the rules given in this paper are true. Underneath the arrow joining any two successive products is given the name of the radiation expelled by the first. This table shows in a striking way the similarities of the three series."[39] ▲

[39] A. S. RUSSELL, "The Periodic System and the Radioelements," *Chemical News*, **107**, January 31, 1913, p. 52.

TABLE 10

Periodic Arrangement of the Radio-elements

Group in Periodic System	VI A	V A	IV A	III A	II A	I A	O	I B	II B	III B	IV B	V B	VI B
Element of highest atomic weight	U	Ta	Th	La	Ra	Cs	Xe	Au	Hg	Tl	Pb	Bi	Te
	Ur 1												
	Ur 2 →α		I₀										
		Ur X₁ →β											
		Ur X₂ →β	Th		Ra →α		Ra Em →α		Ra A →α		Ra B →β	Ra C →β	
			Th →α								Ra D →β	Ra E →β	Ra F →α
											Ra G (Lead)	α+β	
			Ra Th →α		Th X →α		Th Em →α		Th A →α		Th B →β	Th C →β	
				Meso Th 2 →β	Meso Th 1 →O						Th D	α+β	
			Ra Act 1 →β(?)	Act →O	Act X →α		Act Em →α		Act A →α		Act B →β	Act C →β	
			Ra Act 2 →α+β								Act D	α+β	

One month later, Soddy put forward the same conclusions, although the germ of the idea had been stated in a book that he had written two years previously. The situation is admirably summed up by SODDY in his own words.

▼   "In a recent book ("Chemistry of the Radio-elements," p. 30) I stated the rule that held good in several cases, that when the α-particle was expelled the atom passed from a family of even number in the Periodic Table to the next lower-numbered even family, the family of odd number being always missed. Further, in the changes in which the α-particle was not expelled the atom in several cases reverted to its original group, resulting in a curious alternation of properties as the series proceeds. Now, when this occurs, an element of the fourth family, for example, expelling an α-particle and becoming a member of the second family, which after further changes reverts to the fourth family, the two representatives of the fourth family so resulting are not merely similar in chemical properties. They are non-separable by any known process. This applies not merely to the disintegration products of one series but to all the products. Thus, in the fourth group, thorium, uranium X, ionium, radio-thorium, radio-actinium are all chemically non-separable, though they result from three separate series, and the calculated atomic weight varies from 234 to 228.

"In a paper published by A. S. Russell recently (CHEMICAL NEWS, 1913, cvii., 49) some of these generalisations have already been dealt with. Mr. Russell put forward a corollary to my rule for the α-particle which he had previously communicated to me privately in a letter in October, 1912, and which has since been strikingly verified by some of Mr. Fleck's results. Mr. Russell's rule refers to the β-ray and rayless changes, and is that when a β-ray or rayless change occurs the atom changes in chemical nature so as to pass into the family in the Periodic Table next higher in number. That is, the passage in these cases is always from an even to an odd, or from an odd to an even-numbered family. G. von Hevesy (*Phys. Zeit.*, 1913, xiv., 49), who has also been working in Prof. Rutherford's laboratory on the valency of the disintegration products, has put forward very similar views, the difference being that the effect of the β-ray change is considered by him to be the opposite or "polar" to that of the α-ray change, the valency increasing by two after a β-ray change:

"The same questions are also very clearly discussed by K. Fajans, who has been connected with the development of our knowledge in the branch series, but his paper did not come to hand until after this paper was drafted (*Phys. Zeit.*, 1913, xiv., 131 and 136). He takes the view here advocated that the Periodic Law is the expression of the periodic character of radio-active changes, and anticipates some of the other points dealt with in this paper."[40]

▲

[40] F. SODDY, "Radio-elements and the Periodic Law," *Chemical News*, **107**, February 28, 1913, p. 97.

The relationships discovered by Russell, Soddy, and Fajans can thus be summarized; a radioactive element goes back two positions in the periodic table (in the direction of diminishing mass) when it loses an α-particle and goes forward one position in the periodic table (in the direction of increasing mass) when it loses a β-particle. Since the α-particle carries two atomic charges of positive electricity and the β-particle one atomic charge of negative electricity, the position in the periodic table must correspond to different charges within the structure of the atom. The significance of position in the periodic chart in relationship to atomic structure was to await the work of Moseley (Chapter 4), but the Russell-Soddy-Fajans relationship contained the germ of the idea which would soon be developed for all the elements. The name "isotopes" was applied by SODDY in the following words to the products of radioactive changes which had identical properties.

▼ "Every detail of the chemical nature of the members of the known sequences in the uranium, thorium, and actinium series, including the complicated branchings which occur towards the ends, bears out implicitly these two simple rules. Independently of their origin, atomic weights, and radioactive character — that is, of the kinds of change they are about to undergo — all the members of the three disintegration series, which, by the constant application of these rules fall into *the same place* in the periodic table, are chemically completely identical and non-separable from one another. Hence I have termed them *isotopes* or *isotopic elements*."[41]   ▲

The conclusions to be drawn from the experimental results described above are inescapable. Since radioactive change is independent of the state of chemical combination or the physical state of the compound, radioactivity is a characteristic of the atom. In addition, the magnitude of the energy involved in radioactive changes is 100,000 to 1,000,000 times that of the ordinary chemical reaction, which also indicates that the process cannot involve the usual chemical properties of the atom. The ejection of charged helium atoms (α-particles) and electrons (β-particles) from the atom implies that these are constituents of the atom. However, the electrons which are observed as β-rays have a different origin than those discovered by Thomson. As SODDY so aptly stated this observation in his lecture to the Chemical Society in London:

▼ "In another direction there has been a tendency to underrate the unique and unparallelled phenomenon of radioactive change, and to connect what is entirely and solely a development of the new experimental science of radioactivity, with the somewhat older isolation of the electron and the electronic hypothesis of the constitution of matter to which that discovery have given rise. For example, Sir J. J. Thomson in his Romanes Lecture,

[41] F. SODDY, *The Interpretation of Radium* (London: John Murray, Ltd., 1922), p. 229.

1914, says: 'Since the electron can be got from all the chemical elements we may conclude that electrons are a constituent of all the atoms. We have thus made the first steps towards the goal towards which since the time of Prout many chemists have been striving, the proof that the atoms of the chemical elements are built up of simpler atoms — primordial atoms, as they have been called.' The removal of electrons from matter occurs in physical, chemical, and radio-active changes alike, exampled, respectively, by the electrification of a glass rod by friction, the ionization of an electrolyte by solution, and by the β-ray change of radioactive substances. It is only in the latter case, however, that the electron can be regarded as a primordial constituent and the change as transmutational. Even today it is in radio-active phenomena, and in these alone, that the limits reached long ago in chemical analysis of matter have been overstepped and the Rubicon, which a century ago Prout vaulted over so lightly in imagination, has actually been crossed by science."[42]   ▲

The deep-seated source of these particles which resulted from radioactive change is suggested by the fact that there is no way known to affect the rate of disintegration.

Although the first suggestion of the occurrence of isotopes was obtained from the study of radioactive substances, investigations had been in progress and results obtained which hinted at their existence. Sir J. J. Thomson's experiments on the positive rays or "Kanalstrahlen" (cf. Chapter 2) obtained in discharge tubes proved the existence of positively charged atoms, and in several cases gave an indication of the presence of isotopes. It will be recalled that the values of e/m for positive rays depend upon the nature of the gas in the discharge tube. Thomson had conducted experiments on a fraction of air containing a large amount of neon using a discharge tube similar to that shown in Figure 8, and the characteristic parabola was obtained on the photographic plate (cf. Figure 9). Closer inspection of the plate showed that there were actually two parabolas recorded on the photographic plate (Figure 16). THOMSON described these results in an address to the Royal Institution on Friday, January 17, 1913.

▼   "I now turn to the photograph of the lighter constituents; here we find the lines of helium, of neon (very strong), of argon, and in addition there is a line corresponding to an atomic weight 22, which cannot be identified with the line due to any known gas. I thought at first that this line, since its atomic weight is one-half that of CO_2, must be due to a carbonic acid molecule with a double charge of electricity, and on some of the plates a faint line at 44 could be detected. On passing the gas slowly through tubes

[42] F. SODDY, "The Conception of the Chemical Element as Enlarged by the Study of Radio-active Change," *Journal of the Chemical Society*, **115**, 1 (1919).

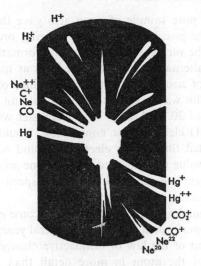

FIGURE 16

The photographic plate from J. J. Thomson's apparatus which indicated the presence of neon isotopes (cf. Figures 8 and 9). Adapted from Aston, Isotopes, 2nd ed. (London: Longmans, Green & Co., 1924).

immersed in liquid air the line at 44 completely disappeared, while the brightness of the one at 22 was not affected.

"The origin of this line presents many points of interest; there are no known gaseous compounds of any of the recognised elements which have this molecular weight. Again, if we accept Mendeleef's Periodic Law, there is no room for a new element with this atomic weight. The fact that this line is bright in the sample when the neon line is extraordinarily bright, and invisible in the other when the neon is comparatively feeble, suggests that it may possibly be a compound of neon and hydrogen, NeH_2, though no direct evidence of the combination of these inert gases has hitherto been found. I have two photographs of the discharge through helium in which there is a strong line, 6, which could be explained by the compound HeH_2, but, as I have never again been able to get these lines, I do not wish to lay much stress on this point. There is, however, the possibility that we may be interpreting Mendeleef's law too rigidly, and that in the neighbourhood of the atomic weight of neon there may be a group of two or more elements with similar properties, just as in another part of the table we have the group iron, nickel, and cobalt. From the relative intensities of the 22 line and the neon line we may conclude that the quantity of the gas giving the 22 line is only a small fraction of the quantity of neon."[43]   ▲

[43] *Proceedings of the Royal Institution*, XX, 593. Quoted with the permission of The Royal Institution.

Later an extremely pure sample of neon also gave the same result, which virtually eliminated the possibility of "NeH$_2$" being present. Moreover, the known chemistry of the rare gases precluded the formation of compounds of any type. The only alternative was that the lines at mass 20 and 22 corresponded to isotopes of neon. The relative intensities of the lines were estimated as 9 to 1, and this was in good agreement with an experimentally determined atomic weight of 20.2. Aston[44] and Dempster went on to develop an apparatus in which (1) elements (or compounds) could be ionized, (2) the positive ions accelerated through an electrostatic and magnetic field, (3) the ions of the same e/m value were focused on the same point, and (4) the "mass spectrum" of the element was recorded. The mass spectrograph has been used since in analysis and atomic weight determinations.

At this stage, the complexity of the atom had become apparent. Rutherford and his associates had performed experiments several years prior to the Russell-Soddy-Fajans statement of the law of radioactive change which indicated the interior architecture of the atom in more detail than had previously been attempted.

SUGGESTED READING

Aston, F. W. "Mass Spectra and Isotopes." London: Edward Arnold and Company, 1942.

Boggs, J. E. "Atomic-weight Variations in Nature," *Journal of Chemical Education*, **32**, 400 (1955).

Cork, J. M. "Radioactivity and Nuclear Physics." New York: D. Van Nostrand Company, Inc., 1947.

Rutherford, E., Chadwick, J., and Ellis, C. D. "Radiations from Radioactive Substances." New York: The Macmillan Company, 1930.

Weeks, M. E. "Discovery of the Elements," Chapter 29, 6th Edition. Easton, Pennsylvania: *Journal of Chemical Education*, 1956. An account of the discovery of the natural radioactive elements.

---

[44] Francis William Aston (1877–1946): His most important work was begun in the Cavendish Laboratory at Cambridge where he became interested in the canal rays produced in discharge tubes. With the aid of a discharge tube designed by J. J. Thomson, Aston eventually developed the mass spectrograph which separates the positively charged particles that constitute the canal rays on the basis of their masses. The most precise values of isotopic weight and composition are obtained by using Aston's method. In 1922 he received the Nobel Prize in chemistry "for his discovery, by means of his mass spectrograph, of the isotopes of a large number of non-radioactive elements, as well as for his discovery of the whole number rule."

CHAPTER 4

The Nuclear Atom

THE KELVIN-THOMSON ATOM

The discharge of electricity through gases as well as the phenomenon of radioactivity presented striking proof of the complexity of atoms and gave impetus to considerations of the inner structure of that which had been postulated by Dalton to be indivisible. Mainly on the basis of radioactive phenomena Lord KELVIN[1] suggested a model for the atom in the following words:

▼ "The properties to be explained are:

"(1) To store a large finite amount of energy in a combination having very narrow stability.

"(2) To expend this energy in shooting off with very great velocity, vitreously and resinously electrified particles.[2]

"In the title of the present communication ('Plan of a Combination of Atoms to Have the Properties of Polonium or Radium'), Polonium means a substance which shoots off vitreously electrified particles abundantly and with very great velocities. Radium means a substance that shoots off in extraordinary abundance both vitreously and resinously electrified particles. From the kinetic theory of gases, it seems certain that every kind of matter has some radioactivity: that is to say, shoots off both vitreously and resin-

---

[1] William Thomson, Lord Kelvin (1824–1907): At the age of 22 he became Professor of Natural Philosophy at Glasgow University where he remained for the rest of his life. He was an accomplished experimenter inventing many instruments which were indispensable for the measurement of electrical phenomena, his main field of concern.

[2] Lord Kelvin applied the terms vitreous and resinous to positively and negatively charged electricity, respectively. Two different types of static electricity can be generated by rubbing glass rods or pieces of rosin, hence the designations vitreous and resinous electricity.

ously electrified particles.[3] Hence it is only in their extraordinarily great abundance and great velocities of shooting, that Polonium and Radium differ from ordinary matter.

"In the present communication I use the word electrion to signify an atom of resinous electricity. . . ."[4]

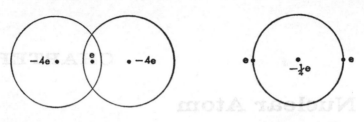

FIGURE 17   FIGURE 18

Lord Kelvin's diagrammatic repre-   *Lord Kelvin's diagrammatic repre-*
sentation of polonium.   *sentation of radium.*

Figures 17 and 18 are adapted from Lord Kelvin, "Plan of a Combination of Atoms to Have the Properties of Polonium or Radium," Philosophical Magazine, 8 (London: Taylor & Francis, Ltd., 1904).

"A plan for molecular structure of Polonium is represented in Figure 17, and may be shortly described as two void atoms[5] held together against their mutual repulsion by a bond consisting of one electrion. A plan of molecular structure for emission of the β rays of Radium is represented in Figure 18, and may be shortly described as two electrions held together against their mutual repulsion by a bond consisting of one void atom.

"In Figure 17 the quantity of vitreous electricity belonging to each of the void atoms is four times the quantity of resinous electricity, e, belonging to an electrion. The quantity of vitreous electricity belonging to the single void atom of Figure 18 is $\frac{1}{4}$e.[6]

"In Figure 17 the total quantity of the two electricities is 8e of vitreous and e of resinous. Hence to make a neutral or unelectrified combination of atoms and electrions we must add a combination electrically equivalent to 7 electrions."[7]   ▲

---

[3] An apparent reference to J. J. Thomson's work on gaseous discharges.

[4] Lord KELVIN, "Plan of a Combination of Atoms to Have the Properties of Polonium or Radium," *Philosophical Magazine*, **8**, 528 (1904).

[5] The term "atom" is used to denote a fundamental particle and does not correspond to the present definition of "atom."

[6] "Plan of a Combination of Atoms to Have the Properties of Polonium or Radium," p. 528.

[7] *Ibid.*, p. 531.

Lord Kelvin goes on to describe the distribution of the 7 positive charges and suggests that they are spread out over the volume of the atom.

Sir J. J. THOMSON in attempting to expand Lord Kelvin's ideas of atomic structure gave the following description of the structure of an atom.

▼   "Starting from the hypothesis that the atom is an aggregation of a number of simpler systems, let us consider what is the nature of one of these systems. We have seen that the corpuscle, whose mass is so much less than that of the atom, is a constituent of the atom. It is natural to regard the corpuscle as a constituent of the primordial system. The corpuscle, however, carries a definite charge of negative electricity, and since with any charge of electricity we always associate an equal charge of the opposite kind, we should expect the negative charge on the corpuscle to be associated with an equal charge of positive electricity."[8]

"Let us picture to ourselves the aggregate as, like the Æpinus atom of Lord Kelvin, consisting of a sphere of uniform positive electrification, and exerting therefore a radial electric force proportional at an internal point to the distance from the centre, and that the very much smaller negatively electrified corpuscles are moving about inside it. The number of corpuscles is the number of units which had gone to make up the aggregate, and the total negative electrification on the corpuscles is equal to the positive electrification on the sphere. To fix our ideas let us take the case shown in Figure 19 of three corpuscles A, B, C, arranged within the sphere at the corners of an equilateral triangle, the centre of the triangle coinciding with the centre of the sphere. First suppose the corpuscles are at rest; they will be in equilibrium when they are at such a distance from the centre of the sphere that the repulsion between the corpuscles, which will evidently be radial, just balances the radial attraction excited on the corpuscles by the positive electrification of the sphere. A simple calculation shows that this will be the case when the distance of the corpuscle from the centre is equal to .57 times the radius of the sphere. Next suppose that the corpuscles, instead of being at rest, are describing circular orbits round the centre of the sphere. Their centrifugal force will carry them farther away from the centre by an amount depending upon the speed with which they are rotating in their orbits. As we increase this speed the distance of the corpuscles from the centre of the sphere will increase until at a certain speed the corpuscles will reach the surface of the sphere; further increases in speed will cause them first to rotate outside the sphere and finally leave the sphere altogether, when the atom will break up.

"In this way we see that the constitution of the aggregate will not be permanent, if the kinetic energy due to the velocity of the corpuscles inside

[8] Sir J. J. THOMSON, *Electricity and Matter* (New Haven: Yale University Press, 1904), p. 93.

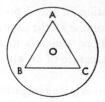

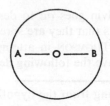

FIGURE 19

FIGURE 20

Lord Kelvin's diagrammatic representation of how three negative charges could form a stable arrangement in a sphere of positive electricity.

Lord Kelvin's diagrammatic representation of how two negative charges could form a stable arrangement in a sphere of positive electricity.

Figures 19 and 20 are adapted from J. J. Thomson, Electricity and Matter (New Haven: Yale University Press, 1904).

the sphere relative to the centre of the sphere exceeds a certain value."[9]

". . . it is desirable to consider more closely the way the corpuscles arrange themselves in the atom. We shall begin with the case where the corpuscles are at rest. The corpuscles are supposed to be in a sphere of uniform positive electrification which produces a radial attractive force on each corpuscle proportional to its distance from the centre of the sphere, and the problem is to arrange the corpuscles in the sphere so that they are in equilibrium under this attraction and their mutual repulsions. If there are only two corpuscles, AB, we can see at once that they will be in equilibrium if placed so that A B and the centre of the sphere are in the same straight line and $OA = OB = \frac{1}{2}$ the radius of the sphere (Figure 20).

"If there are three corpuscles, A B C, they will be in equilibrium of A B C as an equilateral triangle with its centre at O and $OA = OB = OC = (\frac{1}{5})^{1/3}$, or .57 times the radius of the sphere (Figure 19).

"If there are four corpuscles these will be in equilibrium if placed at the angular points of a regular tetrahedron with its centre at the centre of the sphere. In these cases the corpuscles are all on the surface of a sphere concentric with the sphere of positive electrification, and we might suppose that whatever the number of corpuscles the position of equilibrium would be one of symmetrical distribution over the surface of a sphere. Such a distribution would indeed technically be one of equilibrium, but a mathematical calculation shows that unless the number of corpuscles is quite small, say seven or eight at the most, this arrangement is unstable and so can never persist. When the number of corpuscles is greater than this limiting number, the corpuscles break up into two groups. One group containing the smaller number of corpuscles is on the surface of a small body

[9] *Ibid.*, pp. 96–98.

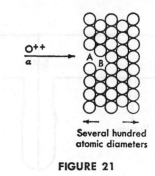

O++
α

A
B

← Several hundred →
atomic diameters

FIGURE 21

An atomic cross section of a metal foil using the Kelvin-Thomson model of the atom.

concentric with the sphere; the remainder are on the surface of a larger concentric body. When the number of corpuscles is still further increased there comes a stage when the equilibrium cannot be stable even with two groups, and the corpuscles now divide themselves into three groups, arranged on the surfaces of concentric shells; and as we go on increasing the number we pass through stages in which more and more groups are necessary for equilibrium. With any considerable number of corpuscles the problem of finding the distribution when in equilibrium becomes too complex for calculation. . . ."[10]

Unfortunately, the Kelvin-Thomson "raisin pudding" model for atomic structures was not able to explain several experimental observations, the most difficult being the manner in which α-particles were scattered by thin metal foils.

If atoms did consist of spheres of positive electricity in which were embedded sufficient electrons to neutralize the positive charge, it might be expected that relatively few α-particles could pass through a metal foil. Even very thin foils are several hundred atoms thick, and, if it is assumed that the atoms are touching each other, it is very doubtful if a positively charged particle (α-particle) could penetrate more than a few atomic diameters of positive charge before being stopped (Figure 21). Even by assuming that there are imperfections in the crystal structure of the foil; e.g., atoms A and B of Figure 21 missing, it is doubtful if this imperfection would continue through the entire thickness of the foil. However, the experiments of Geiger and Marsden[11] show that a beam of α-particles can pass through a thin metal foil and, perhaps more interestingly, that some α-particles are deflected at all possible angles with

[10] *Ibid.*, pp. 111–113.
[11] Ernest Marsden (1889–   ): Professor of Physics at Victoria University College, Wellington, New Zealand, and later Secretary of the Department of Scientific and Industrial Research, New Zealand.

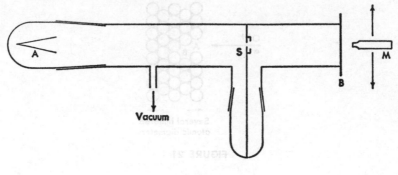

FIGURE 22

The apparatus used by Hans Geiger to study the scattering of α-particles as they passed through a metal foil.

respect to the undeflected beam. Geiger originally measured the scattering angle in an apparatus similar to that shown in Figure 22. A glass tube about two meters long contained a radioactive source of α-particles at one end (A). The beam of α-particles passed through a slit S, and the image of the slit appeared on the zinc sulfide screen B attached to the other end of the tube. The scintillations at different points on the screen were observed with the aid of a microscope M, the position of which could be read on a scale attached to the apparatus. The tube could be evacuated, and with a good vacuum practically no scintillations were observed outside of the geometrical image of the slit. A thin foil of metal could be placed over the slit, and, by moving the microscope along the whole screen and counting the number of scintillations at definite intervals, a plot of the distribution of the α-particles from the center of the beam was obtained (Figure 23). Curve A of Figure 23 shows the angle of scatter for a vacuum with no foil covering the slit. The slight scattering was attributed by Geiger to traces of air remaining in the tube. Curves B and C were obtained with one and two gold foils over the slit. GEIGER concludes his report of the experiment in the following words:

▼   "The observations just described give direct evidence that there is a very marked scattering of the α-rays in passing through matter, whether gaseous or solid. It will be noticed that some of the α-particles after passing through the very thin leaves — the stopping power of one leaf corresponding to about 1 mm. of air — were deflected through quite an appreciable angle."[12]

▲

[12] H. GEIGER, "On the Scattering of the α-Particles by Matter," *Proceedings of the Royal Society*, **81**, 177 (1908).

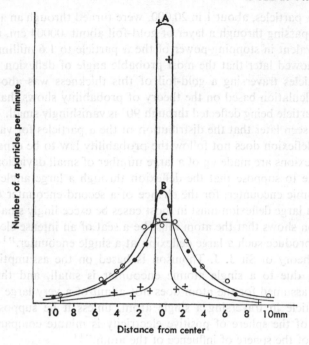

FIGURE 23

The results of Geiger's experiment on the scattering angle of α-particles.
Adapted from H. Geiger, "On the Scattering of the α-Particles by Matter,"
Proceedings of the Royal Society, 81 (London: The Royal Society, 1908).

In other experiments Geiger and Marsden showed that the scattering of
α-particles depends upon the atomic weight of the metal comprising the foil.

THE RUTHERFORD ATOM

In 1911 RUTHERFORD attempted to explain the results from these scattering
experiments by suggesting a different theory of atomic structure in the following
manner:

▼ "It has generally been supposed that the scattering of a pencil of α or β
rays in passing through a thin plate of matter is the result of a multitude of
small scatterings by the atoms of matter traversed. The observations, however, of Geiger and Marsden on the scattering of α rays indicate that some
of the α particles must suffer a deflexion of more than a right angle at a
single encounter. They found, for example, that a small fraction of the

incident α particles, about 1 in 20,000, were turned through an average angle of 90° in passing through a layer of gold-foil about .00004 cm. thick, which was equivalent in stopping-power of the α particle to 1.6 millimetres of air. Geiger showed later that the most probable angle of deflexion for a pencil of α particles traversing a gold-foil of this thickness was about 0°.87. A simple calculation based on the theory of probability shows that the chance of an α particle being deflected through 90° is vanishingly small. In addition, it will be seen later that the distribution of the α particles for various angles of large deflexion does not follow the probability law to be expected if such large deflexions are made up of a large number of small deviations. It seems reasonable to suppose that the deflexion through a large angle is due to a single atomic encounter, for the chance of a second encounter of a kind to produce a large deflexion must in most cases be exceedingly small. A simple calculation shows that the atom must be a seat of an intense electric field in order to produce such a large deflexion at a single encounter."[13]

"The theory of Sir J. J. Thomson is based on the assumption that the scattering due to a single atomic encounter is small, and the particular structure assumed for the atom does not admit of a very large deflexion of an α particle in traversing a single atom, unless it be supposed that the diameter of the sphere of positive electricity is minute compared with the diameter of the sphere of influence of the atom."[14]   ▲

Thus, the atom as we know it today was conceived. The suggestion that the region of the atom which caused deflection of α-particles was very small in comparison to the size of the atom and carried the same charge as the α-particle readily explained the results of Geiger and Marsden. A thin sheet of foil composed of nuclear atoms still is several hundred atomic diameters thick, but now the deflecting regions of the atom (the nuclei) are relatively far apart, and the majority of the α-particles can pass through the foil with little or no deflection (A of Figure 24). Occasionally an α-particle from the beam will encounter an atomic nucleus in the foil directly in the line of flight (B of Figure 24), and the α-particle will be deflected back parallel to its original path. It would be expected that all possible deflections are possible between these two extremes. Using data obtained for the 180° deflection, RUTHERFORD estimated the size of the nucleus by arguing as follows:

▼   "Consider an atom which contains a charge $\pm Ne$ at its centre surrounded by a sphere of electrification containing a charge $\mp Ne$ supposed uniformly distributed throughout a sphere of radius R. e is the fundamental unit of

[13] E. RUTHERFORD, "The Scattering of α and β Particles by Matter and the Structure of the Atom," *Philosophical Magazine*, 21, 669 (1911).
[14] *Ibid.*, p. 669.

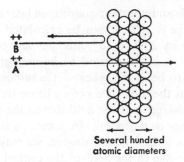

Several hundred
atomic diameters

FIGURE 24

An atomic cross section of a metal foil using the Rutherford model of the atom.

charge, which in this paper is taken as 4.65×10^{-10} E.S. unit. We shall suppose that for distances less than 10^{-12} cm. the central charge and also the charge on the α particle may be supposed to be concentrated at a point. It will be shown that the main deductions from the theory are independent of whether the central charge is supposed to be positive or negative. For convenience, the sign will be assumed to be positive. The question of the stability of the atom proposed need not be considered at this stage, for this will obviously depend upon the minute structure of the atom, and on the motion of the constituent charged parts.

"In order to form some idea of the forces required to deflect an α particle through a large angle, consider an atom containing a positive charge Ne at its centre, and surrounded by a distribution of negative electricity Ne uniformly distributed within a sphere of radius R. The electric force X and the potential V at a distance r from the centre of an atom for a point inside the atom, are given by

$$X = Ne \left(\frac{1}{r^2} - \frac{r}{R^3} \right)$$

$$V = Ne \left(\frac{1}{r} - \frac{3}{2R} + \frac{r^2}{2R^3} \right).$$

Suppose an α particle of mass m and velocity u and charge E shot directly towards the centre of the atom. It will be brought to rest at a distance b from the centre given by

$$\frac{1}{2} mu^2 = NeE \left(\frac{1}{b} - \frac{3}{2R} + \frac{b^2}{2R^3} \right).$$

It will be seen that b is an important quantity in later calculations. Assuming that the central charge is $100e$, it can be calculated that the value of b for an α particle of velocity 2.09×10^9 cms. per second is about 3.4×10^{-2} cm. In this calculation b is supposed to be very small compared with R. Since R is supposed to be of the order of the radius of the atom, vis. 10^{-8} cm., it is obvious that the α particle before being turned back penetrates so close to the central charge, that the field due to the uniform distribution of negative electricity may be neglected. In general, a simple calculation shows that for all deflexions greater than a degree, we may without sensible error suppose the deflexion due to the field of the central charge alone. Possible single deviations due to the negative electricity, if distributed in the form of corpuscles, are not taken into account at this stage of the theory. It will be shown later that its effect is in general small compared with that due to the central field." [15]   ▲

Rutherford's estimate of the size of a nucleus in comparison to the size of the atom indicates the disparity of the relative sizes shown in Figure 24. If the nucleus of the atoms represented in Figure 24 were the size of a period on this printed page, the nuclei would be about two inches apart. Thus, an α-particle, which would also be the size of a period on this scale, would have little difficulty going through a foil. RUTHERFORD summed up his classic paper with the following words:

▼   "In comparing the theory outlined in this paper with the experimental results, it has been supposed that the atom consists of a central charge supposed concentrated at a point, and that the large single deflexions of the α and β particles are mainly due to their passage through the strong central field. The effect of the equal and opposite compensating charge supposed distributed uniformly throughout a sphere has been neglected. Some of the evidence in support of these assumptions will now be briefly considered. For concreteness, consider the passage of a high speed α particle through an atom having a positive central charge Ne, and surrounded by a compensating charge of N electrons. Remembering that the mass, momentum, and kinetic energy of the α particle are very large compared with the corresponding values for an electron in rapid motion, it does not seem possible from dynamic considerations that an α particle can be deflected through a large angle by a close approach to an electron, even if the latter be in rapid motion and constrained by strong electrical forces. It seems reasonable to suppose that the chance of single deflexions through a large angle due to this cause, if not zero, must be exceedingly small compared with that due to the central charge.

[15] *Ibid.*, p. 670.

"It is of interest to examine how far the experimental evidence throws light on the question of the extent of the distribution of the central charge. Suppose, for example, the central charge to be composed of N unit charges distributed over such a volume that the large single deflexions are mainly due to the constituent charges and not to the external field produced by the distribution. It has been shown that the fraction of the α particles scattered through a large angle is proportional to $(NeE)^2$, where Ne is the central charge concentrated at a point and E the charge on the deflected particle. If, however, this charge is distributed in single units, the fraction of the α particles scattered through a given angle is proportional to Ne^2 instead of N^2e^2. In this calculation, the influence of mass of the constituent particle has been neglected, and account has only been taken of its electric field. Since it has been shown that the value of the central point charge for gold must be about 100, the value of the distributed charge required to produce the same proportion of single deflexions through a large angle should be at least 10,000. Under these conditions the mass of the constituent particle would be small compared with that of the α particle, and the difficulty arises of the production of large single deflexions at all. In addition, with such a large distributed charge, the effect of compound scattering is relatively more important than that of single scattering. For example, the probable small angle of deflexion of a pencil of α particles passing through a thin gold foil would be much greater than that experimentally observed by Geiger. The large and small angle scattering could not then be explained by the assumption of a central charge of the same value. Considering the evidence as a whole, it seems simplest to suppose that the atom contains a central charge distributed through a very small volume, and that the large single deflexions are due to the central charge as a whole, and not to its constituents. At the same time, the experimental evidence is not precise enough to negate the possibility that a small fraction of the positive charge may be carried by satellites extending some distance from the centre. Evidence on this point could be obtained by examining whether the same central charge is required to explain the large single deflexions of α and β particles; for the α particle must approach much closer to the centre of the atom than the β particle of average speed to suffer the same large deflexion."[16]   ▲

ATOMIC NUMBERS AND THEIR SIGNIFICANCE

The observation that the magnitude of α-particle scattering depends upon the atomic weight of the scattering atom suggested that the charge on the nucleus increases with increasing atomic weight. A precise measurement of this increase

[16] *Ibid.*, p. 686.

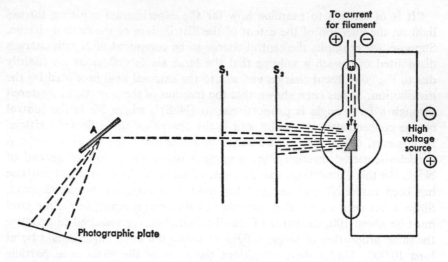

The generation of X-rays. Electrons are accelerated in an evacuated discharge tube and strike a metal target which in turn generates X-rays. The X-rays are given off in a variety of angles and to be useful a narrow beam is required. This is obtained by taking the radiation that passes through slits S_1 and S_2.

in charge could not be made from the data on α-particle scattering, but two years after Rutherford had suggested his theory of the nuclear atom Moseley's[17] work with X-rays provided the answer to this question.

The nature and origin of X-radiation have been the source of lively investigations by many workers since the time Röntgen first observed the phenomenon. X-Rays can be generated by causing a high velocity electron beam to strike a target (Figure 25). The X-rays emanate from the anode in a wide beam, but a narrow beam can be obtained by placing one or two lead slits in front of the tube. X-Rays are not deflected by a magnetic or electrostatic field, cause a fluorescent screen to glow, ionize gases through which they pass, and cause exposure of photographic plates. In general, matter will retard an X-ray beam, and the decrease in beam intensity depends on the nature of the atoms and the thickness of the sample. The properties of X-rays suggest that they are electromagnetic in nature; i.e., they obey the same laws as a beam of visible light, and a beam of X-rays can be separated into its component parts in much

[17] Henry Gwynn Jefferys Moseley (1887–1915): Moseley studied under Rutherford at Manchester and began to do research at Oxford before the first World War. He was twenty-six when he formulated the sequence of elements based upon the atomic number as determined from X-ray experiments. Two years later he was killed on the ill-fated British expedition to the Dardanelles.

the same manner as a beam of white light can be separated into light of various frequencies. Ordinary light can be defracted by a glass or a quartz prism, but the very short wave length of X-rays requires the use of a crystalline substance. The defracting units in these crystals are the atoms of the substance which are ordered in a regular array. Moseley in his investigations used a crystal of potassium ferrocyanide as his defracting unit (*A* of Figure 25). The defracted X-rays were then detected by their ability to blacken a photographic plate.

Mosely and Darwin showed that X-rays from a tube containing a platinum target consist of two types of radiation. One type of radiation consisted of X-rays of indefinite wave length; i.e., it was a mixture of X-rays with many different wave lengths. In addition to this they observed X-rays of discrete wave lengths (monochromatic) which appeared to be characteristic of the element used to construct the anode of the X-ray tube.

In an attempt to show that the monochromatic X-rays were characteristic of an element, Moseley investigated the X-rays emitted from anodes prepared from various elements. Initially the twelve elements from calcium through zinc (excluding scandium) in the periodic classification of elements were investigated, and in each case only two lines (X-rays of two distinct wave lengths) were observed. Moreover, the wave lengths of these lines depend upon (or were "characteristic "of) the nature of the element (Table 11). Figure 26 shows the original plate from Moseley's paper. The stronger of the two characteristic lines was called the α-line and the weaker line the β-line.[18] The spectrum of the brass sample shows the presence of both copper and zinc lines as expected. The cobalt sample which Moseley used contained 0.8 per cent of iron and 2.2 per cent of nickel, and the recorded spectrum shows the presence of these elements. This led MOSELEY to speculate as follows:

▼ "The prevalence of lines due to impurities suggests that this may prove a powerful method of chemical analysis. Its advantage over ordinary spectroscopic methods lies in the simplicity of the spectra and the impossibility of one substance masking the radiation from another. It may even lead to the discovery of missing elements, as it will be possible to predict the position of their characteristic lines."[19]   ▲

A glance at Figure 26 indicates that the wave length of the characteristic radiation proceeds in a regular manner from an element in one position in the periodic arrangement of the elements to the next. It is this regularity that MOSELEY described in a quantitative manner.

[18] These designations are not to be confused with α- and β-particles. α and β happen to be the first two letters in the Greek alphabet and are often used to differentiate between the first and second members of a group.

[19] H. G. J. MOSELEY, "The High Frequency Spectra of the Elements," *Philosophical Magazine*, **26**, 1024 (1913).

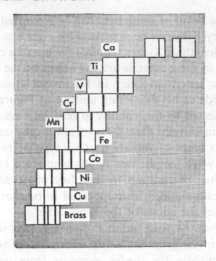

FIGURE 26

Moseley's X-ray spectra of the elements in the first transition series. Note that the brass spectrum contains the two copper lines; the other lines present are due to other constituents of the brass. The cobalt sample was contaminated with iron and nickel as indicated by its spectrum. Adapted from H. G. J. Moseley, "The High Frequency Spectra of the Elements," Philosophical Magazine, 26 (London: Taylor & Francis, Ltd., 1913).

▼ "A discussion will now be given of the meaning of the wave-lengths of the principal spectrum-line α. In Table 11 the values are given of the quantity

$$Q = \sqrt{\frac{\nu}{\frac{3}{4}\nu_0}}$$

ν being the frequency of the radiation α, and ν_0 the fundamental frequency of ordinary line spectra. The latter is obtained from Rydberg's wave-number, $N_0 = \frac{\nu}{C} = 109{,}720$. The reason for introducing this particular constant will be given later. It is at once evident that Q increases by a constant amount as we pass from one element to the next, using the chemical order of the elements in the periodic system. Except in the case of nickel and cobalt, this is also the order of the atomic weights. While, however, Q increases uniformly the atomic weights vary in an arbitrary manner, so that an exception in their order does not come as a surprise. We have here a proof that there is in the atom a fundamental quantity, which increases by

TABLE 11

Element	Line	λ	$Q = (\nu/\tfrac{3}{4}\nu_0)^{1/2}$	N atomic number	Atomic wt.
Calcium	α	3.368×10^{-8}	19.00	20	40.09
	β	3.094			
Scandium	—	—	—	21	44.1
Titanium	α	2.758	20.99	22	48.1
	β	2.524			
Vanadium	α	2.519	21.96	23	51.06
	β	2.297			
Chromium	α	2.301	22.98	24	52.0
	β	2.093			
Manganese	α	2.111	23.99	25	54.93
	β	1.918			
Iron	α	1.946	24.99	26	55.85
	β	1.765			
Cobalt	α	1.798	26.00	27	58.97
	β	1.629			
Nickel	α	1.662	27.04	28	58.68
	β	1.506			
Copper	α	1.549	28.01	29	63.57
	β	1.402			
Zinc	α	1.445	29.01	30	65.37
	β	1.306			

regular steps as we pass from one element to the next. This quantity can only be the charge on the central positive nucleus, of the existence of which we already have definite proof. Rutherford has shown, from the magnitude of the scattering of α particles by matter, that this nucleus carries a $+$ charge approximately equal to that of A/2 electrons, where A is the atomic weight. Barkla, from the scattering of X rays by matter, has shown that the number of electrons in an atom is roughly A/2, which for an electrically neutral atom comes to the same thing. Now atomic weights increase on the average by about 2 units at a time, and this strongly suggests the view that N increases from atom to atom always by a single electronic unit. We are therefore led by experiment to the view that N is the same as the number of the place occupied by the element in the periodic system. This atomic number is then H 1, for He 2 for Li 3 ... for Ca 20 ... for Zn 30, etc. This theory was originated by Brock and since used by Bohr. We can confidently predict that in the few cases in which the order of the atomic weight A clashes with the chemical order of the periodic system, the chemical properties are governed by N; while A is itself probably a complicated function of N. The very close similarity between the X-ray spectra of the different elements shows that these radiations originate inside the atom, and have no direct connexion with the complicated light-spectra and chemical properties which are governed by the structure of its surface.

"We will now examine the relation

$$Q = \sqrt{\frac{\nu}{\frac{3}{4}\nu_0}}$$

more closely. So far the argument has relied on the fact that Q is a quantity which increases from atom to atom by equal steps. Now Q has been obtained by multiplying $\nu^{1/2}$ by a constant factor so chosen to make the steps equal to unity. We have, therefore,

$$Q = N - k,$$

where k is a constant. Hence the frequency ν varies as $(N - k)^2$. If N for calcium is really 20 then $k = 1$."[20]   ▲

About one year later Moseley completed his investigations of the X-ray spectra of thirty more elements and showed that the same relationship held for much heavier and much lighter elements than those originally investigated. From the relationships noted above it is obvious that the atomic number is a function of $\sqrt{\nu}$ for a given X-ray line. Moseley's data are plotted graphically in Figure 27 for the K series (both K_α and K_β) and for a new series of X-ray lines, the L series. The latter series consists of five lines but only four of the lines are plotted. Careful inspection of the data indicates that space has been assigned to elements that were not known to exist. Had these vacancies been ignored the straight line plot shown in Figure 27 would have contained discontinuities. MOSELEY describes these vacancies as follows:

▼   "In Fig. 27 the spectra of the elements are arranged on horizontal lines spaced at equal distances. The order chosen for the elements is the order of the atomic weights, except in the cases of A,[21] Co, and Te, where this clashes with the order of the chemical properties. Vacant lines have been left for an element between Mo and Ru, an element between Nd and Sa, and an element between W and Os, none of which are yet known, while Tm, which Welsbach has separated into two constituents, is given two lines. This is equivalent to assigning to successive elements a series of successive characteristic integers. On this principle the integer N for Al, the thirteenth element, has been taken to be 13, and the values of N then assumed by the other elements are given on the left-hand side of Fig. 27. This proceeding is justified by the fact that it introduces perfect regularity into the X-ray

[20] *Ibid.*, pp. 1030–1032.
[21] Argon, the present symbol for this element is Ar.

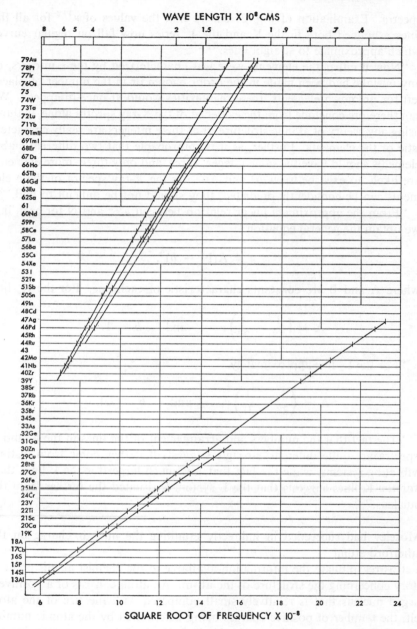

WAVE LENGTH X 10⁸ CMS

SQUARE ROOT OF FREQUENCY X 10⁻⁸

FIGURE 27

A graphical representation of Moseley's data. Adapted from H. G. J. Moseley, "The High Frequency Spectra of the Elements. Part II," Philosophical Magazine, 27 (London: Taylor & Francis, Ltd., 1914).

spectra. Examination of Fig. 27 shows that the values of $\nu^{1/2}$ for all the lines examined both in the K and the L series now fall on regular curves which approximate to straight lines."[22]

"Now if either the elements were not characterized by these integers, or any mistake had been made in the order chosen or in the number" of places left for unknown elements, these regularities would at once disappear. We can therefore conclude from the evidence of the X-ray spectra alone, without using any theory of atomic structure, that these integers are really character-istic of the elements. Further, as it is improbable that two different stable elements should have the same integer, three, and only three, more elements are likely to exist between Al and Au. As the X-ray spectra of these ele-ments can be confidently predicted, they should not be difficult to find."[23]

"From the approximate linear relation between $\nu^{1/2}$ and N for each line we obtain the general equation

$$\nu = A(N - b)^2,$$

where A and B are constants characteristic of each line. For the K_α line

$$A = \left(\frac{1}{1^2} - \frac{1}{2^2}\right)\nu_0 \quad \text{and} \quad b = 1.$$

"For the L_α line approximately

$$A = \left(\frac{1}{2^2} - \frac{1}{3^2}\right)\nu_0 \quad \text{and} \quad b = 7.4.$$

"The fact that the numbers and arrangement of the lines in the K and L spectra are quite different, strongly suggests that they come from distinct vibrating systems, while the fact that b is much larger for the L lines than for the K lines suggests that the L system is situated the further from the nucleus."[24]   ▲

Moseley had succeeded in indirectly counting the nuclear charge on the Rutherford atom!

Let us recapitulate the information available to the chemist at this point in history concerning the structure of the atom. An atom consists of a positively charged nucleus that is relatively small compared with the size of the atom itself, the number of positive charges being determined by the atomic number of the element. The first element in the periodic chart, hydrogen, contains one

[22] H. G. J. MOSELEY, "The High Frequency Spectra of the Elements. Part II," *Philosophical Magazine*, **27**, 709 (1914).

[23] *Ibid.*, p. 711.

[24] *Ibid.*, pp. 712–713.

positive charge in its nucleus, and, therefore, all other elements must contain a whole number of hydrogen nuclei (or protons) equivalent to its atomic number. [It would appear that Prout's hypothesis (Chapter 1) was verified.] Since the weight of a proton is 1836 times that of an electron, the mass of the atom is concentrated in the nucleus. It will be recalled that some atoms emit electrons (β-particles) in the course of radioactive decay and it is reasonable to suspect that these particles are to be found in the nucleus. The electrons emitted from the nuclei are not to be confused with the electrons that are found outside of the nucleus which compensate for the nuclear charge. These ideas were emphasized by RUTHERFORD in his Bakerian Lecture before the Royal Society.

▼   "We also have strong reason for believing that the nuclei of atoms contain electrons as well as positively charged bodies, and that the positive charge on the nucleus represents the excess positive charge. It is of interest to note the very different role played by the electrons in the outer and inner atom. In the former case, the electrons arrange themselves at a distance from the nucleus, controlled no doubt mainly by the charge on the nucleus and the interaction of their own fields. In the case of the nucleus, the electron forms a very close and powerful combination with the positively charged units and, as far as we know, there is a region just outside the nucleus where no electron is in stable equilibrium. While no doubt each of the external electrons acts as a point charge in considering the forces between it and the nucleus, this cannot be the case for the electron in the nucleus itself. It is to be anticipated that under the intense forces in the latter, the electrons are much deformed and the forces may be of a very different character from those to be expected from an undeformed electron, as in the outer atom. It may be for this reason that the electron can play such a different part in the two cases and yet form stable systems."[25]   ▲

Thus, in a neutral atom the atomic number indicates the number of extra-nuclear electrons as well as the number of uncompensated protons in the nucleus. By using this information the constitution of any isotope of any element can be deduced. The first ten elements (including isotopes) in the periodic classification and the distribution of protons and electrons in the atom are given in Table 12. The relative weights of the isotopes can be determined to a high degree of precision by using mass spectroscopic techniques, but the number listed for the mass of the isotope is the nearest whole number for the sake of convenience. Thus, for example, the isotope of boron with mass 11 has an atomic number of 5 (as do all isotopes of boron), and to have an atom of this weight (11 units) there must be 11 protons in the nucleus. However, an atomic

[25] Sir E. RUTHERFORD, "Nuclear Constitution of Atoms," *Proceedings of the Royal Society*, **97**, 377 (1920).

TABLE 12

Distribution of Electrons and Protons in Some Atoms

Element	Mass	Atomic number	Nuclear Structure		No. of extranuclear electrons
			No. of protons	No. of electrons	
Hydrogen	1	1	1	0	1
Helium	2	2	2	0	2
Lithium	6	3	6	3	3
"	7	3	7	4	3
Beryllium	8	4	8	4	4
"	9	4	9	5	4
"	10	4	10	6	4
Boron	10	5	10	5	5
"	11	5	11	6	5
Carbon	12	6	12	6	6
"	13	6	13	7	6
Nitrogen	14	7	14	7	7
"	15	7	15	8	7
Oxygen	16	8	16	8	8
"	17	8	17	9	8
"	18	8	18	10	8
Fluorine	19	9	19	10	9
Neon	20	10	20	10	10
"	21	10	21	11	10
"	22	10	22	12	10

number of 5 indicates only 5 positive charges in the nucleus; therefore, there must be 6 electrons in the nucleus to decrease the nuclear charge to 5. To complete the structure of the neutral atom, 5 extranuclear electrons are necessary. This isotope of boron differs from the isotope with mass 10 only in that there is one proton and one less electron in the nucleus. Although Table 12 lists only the first ten elements, the constitution of all the other elements can be derived by the preceding arguments. It would thus appear that the question of the composition of the nucleus is answered and no more thought need be expended on it. Fortunately, or unfortunately, as the case may be, this situation did not prevail for long.

NEUTRONS

Several scientists observed that beryllium and boron emitted a very penetrating radiation when bombarded with α-particles, and initially this was assumed to be a form of γ-radiation. Further experiments showed that the "beryllium radiation" was many times more energetic than any known γ-radiation. In addition, it was observed that protons were ejected from a block of paraffin wax placed in a beam of the "beryllium radiation" (Figure 28), but

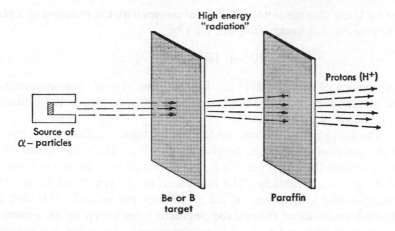

FIGURE 28

The bombardment of either beryllium or boron by particles produced a high energy radiation which was detected by the protons liberated by it from a block of paraffin.

this radiation passed through one inch of lead and lost less than one-half of its intensity.

Chadwick[26] suggested that, if the "beryllium radiation" consisted of a beam of particles, a great many of the theoretical difficulties which arose on assuming that it was electromagnetic in nature disappeared. The particles which make up the beam must be uncharged (or at least their field of influence is very small) since they can pass through the collection of positively charged and negatively charged particles which constitute atoms without disturbing them (or itself) or transferring energy. The name "neutron" was suggested for this particle. Furthermore, if the mass of the neutron was approximately the same as that of the proton and its velocity sufficiently high, it could set the lighter nuclei such as hydrogen in motion by direct collision. CHADWICK estimated the mass of the neutron using the following argument:

▼ "It was stated that boron bombarded by α-particles of polonium also emits a radiation which ejects protons from materials containing hydrogen. Further examination showed that this radiation behaves in all respects like that from beryllium, and it must therefore be assumed to consist of neutrons. It is probable that the neutrons are emitted from the isotope B^{11},

[26] James Chadwick (1891–   ): Professor of Physics at the University of Liverpool. In 1935 he received the Nobel Prize in physics for "his discovery of the neutron."

for we know that the isotope B^{10} disintegrates with the emission of a proton. The process of disintegration will then be

$$B^{11} + He^4 \rightarrow N^{14} + n^1$$

The masses of B^{11} and N^{14} are known from Aston's measurements, and the further data required for the deduction of the mass of the neutron can be obtained by experiment."[27]

"The range of the protons ejected by the boron radiation was measured in the same way as with the beryllium radiation. The effects observed were much smaller than with beryllium, and it was difficult to measure the range of the protons accurately. The maximum range was about 16 cm. in air, corresponding to a velocity of 2.5×10^9 cm. per second. This then is the maximum velocity of the neutron liberated from boron by an α-particle of polonium of velocity 1.59×10^9 cm. per second. Assuming that momentum is conserved in the collision, the velocity of the recoiling N^{14} nucleus can be calculated, and we then know the kinetic energies of all the particles concerned in the disintegration process. The energy equation of the process is

Mass of B^{11} + mass of He^4 + K.E. of He^4 =

  mass of N^{14} + mass of n^1 + K.E. of N^{14} + K.E. of n^1.

The masses are $B^{11} = 11.00825 \pm 0.0016$; $He^4 = 4.00106 \pm 0.006$; $N^{14} = 14.0042 \pm 0.0028$. The kinetic energies in mass units are α-particle $= 0.00565$; neutron $= 0.0035$; and nitrogen nucleus $= 0.00061$. We find therefore that the mass of the neutron is 1.0067. Allowing for the errors in the mass measurements it appears that the mass of the neutron cannot be less than 1.003, and that it probably lies between 1.005 and 1.008.

"Such a value for the mass of the neutron is to be expected if the neutron consists of a proton and an electron, and it lends strong support to this view. Since the sum of the masses of the proton and electron is 1.0078, the binding energy, or mass defect, of the neutron is about 1 to 2 million electron volts. This is quite a reasonable value. We may suppose that the proton and electron form a small dipole, or we may take the more attractive picture of a proton embedded in an electron. On either view, we may expect the 'radius' of the neutron to be a few times 10^{-13} cm."[28]   ▲

With the discovery of the neutron, the necessity of "nuclear electrons" was eliminated and the mass of an atomic nucleus was determined by the number of neutrons plus protons, the former corresponding in number to the number of nuclear electrons previously suggested (cf. Table 12). The characteristics of

[27] J. CHADWICK, "Existence of a Neutron," *Proceedings of the Royal Society*, **136A**, 701 (1932).
[28] *Ibid.*, pp. 701–702.

the elementary particles constituting an atom as determined by the most modern and refined methods are listed in Table 13. Within recent years some 30 sub-

TABLE 13

The Characteristics of the Fundamental
Subatomic Particles

Name	Mass (atomic weight units)		Electric charge (coulombs)
Electron	0.0005486	−	1.60207×10^{-19}
Proton	1.007581	+	1.60207×10^{-19}
Neutron	1.00893	0	0.0

atomic particles have been observed, but a description of these experiments would make our present discussion unnecessarily long and would contribute little more to the object of this volume.

As was pointed out by Rutherford, the atom consists of two portions: the nucleus and the extranuclear portion. Although Moseley's atomic number concerns itself with the number of positive charges in the nucleus, it indirectly determines the extranuclear structure of the atom since for the neutral atom it also reflects the number of extranuclear electrons. The number and distribution of the latter give an element its characteristic chemical properties and for the average chemist are often the more important consideration.

SUGGESTED READING

Gilreath, E. S., *Fundamental Concepts of Inorganic Chemistry*, Chapter 2. New York: McGraw-Hill Book Company, Inc., 1958.

Lavrakas, V., "A History of the Neutron," *Journal of Chemical Education*, **29**, 281 (1952).

Taylor, W. H., "J. A. R. Newlands: A Pioneer in Atomic Numbers," *Journal of Chemical Education*, **26**, 491 (1949).

CHAPTER 5

Extranuclear Electrons

OPTICAL SPECTRA

In our discussion of nuclear structure we stressed the importance of the X-ray spectra of the elements in elucidating the nature of the nucleus. An investigation of spectra in a slightly different region of the electromagnetic spectrum, the optical region, led to the discovery of numerical relationships that were as important in describing extranuclear atomic structure as those discovered by Moseley for nuclear structure. Before proceeding with a description of the extranuclear structure of the atom, it is perhaps important to discuss optical spectra.

It is well-known that a beam of light can be separated into its component wave lengths by a prism or a diffraction grating. The most common example of this phenomenon is the separation of sunlight by finely dispersed water droplets into the familiar "rainbow of colors." This observation coupled with the fact that samples of different elements emit light of different colors when heated or sparked is the foundation of atomic spectra. The apparatus for recording spectra is shown schematically in Figure 29. Light from a source of radiation is allowed to fall upon a narrow slit, and the beam of light passing through the slit is broken into its component wave lengths which are recorded on a photographic plate. The "line" which appears on the photographic plate is an image of the slit, and the position of the line on the photographic plate depends upon the wave length of light; light of the shortest wave length is deflected more by the prism than light of longer wave length. By suitable experimental techniques it is possible to calibrate this instrument (the spectrograph) to determine the wave length of a particular line by its relative position on the photographic plate. In general photographic plates are used to record

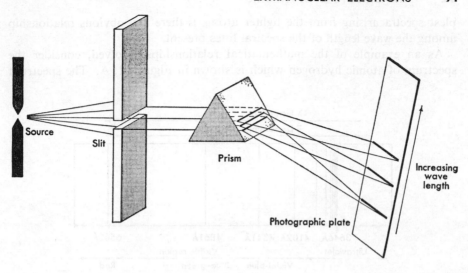

FIGURE 29

The essential components of a spectrograph.

the positions of the spectral lines since many of these lines lie beyond the
human visual range. The source of radiation can be any sample of matter
that has been energetically excited, i.e. by heating, by an electrical spark through
a gas, or by an electric spark between electrodes made of the material under
investigation.

The spectra of the elements consist of distinctive groups of lines which can
be used for identification purposes, since no two elements have the same distribution of spectral lines. Atomic spectra are much more complex than
Moseley's X-ray spectra (compare, for example, the optical spectrum of calcium in Figure 30 with its X-ray spectrum in Figure 26), and only in the sim-

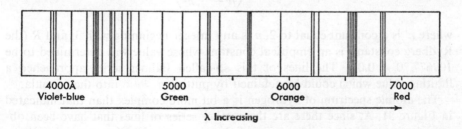

FIGURE 30

The atomic spectrum of calcium in the visible region.

plest spectra arising from the lighter atoms is there any obvious relationship among the wave length of the spectral lines present.

As an example of the mathematical relationships involved, consider the spectrum of atomic hydrogen which is shown in Figure 31, A. The spectrum

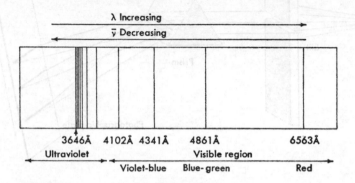

FIGURE 31, A

The Balmer series of lines in the spectrum of hydrogen atoms. The series limit occurs at 3545Å.

consists of a series of lines starting at long wave lengths (the red end of the spectrum) and proceeding in a regular manner toward the short wave length (the blue end) to what is called the series limit. In general the regularities in spectral lines are more easily expressed in terms of the wave number ($\bar{\nu}$) of the line which is the reciprocal of the wave length ($\bar{\nu} = 1/\lambda$). Balmer was the first to show that lines of this series in the spectrum of hydrogen were related by the expression

$$\bar{\nu} = R \left(\frac{1}{n'^2} - \frac{1}{n^2} \right) \tag{1}$$

where n' is a constant equal to 2, n is any integer beginning with 3, and R (the Rydberg constant) is an empirical constant whose value was determined to be 109677.70 ± 0.04. The lines of this so-called Balmer series approached a limiting value which could be obtained by putting $n = \infty$ into the formula.

The atomic spectrum of hydrogen is a bit more complex than that indicated in Figure 31, A, since there are three other series of lines that have been observed outside of the visible region of the spectrum. The Lyman series occurs in the ultraviolet region of the spectrum, but the Paschen and Brackett series are in the infrared region. The position of each line in these series can be

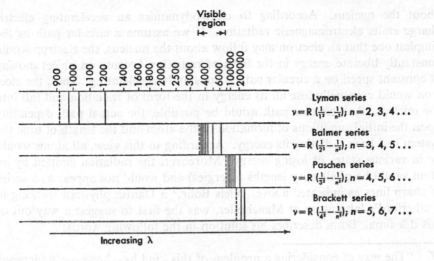

FIGURE 31, B

The four series of spectral lines for hydrogen atoms. The series have been separated for clarity, and the dotted lines represent the series limit.

obtained by substituting

$$n' = 1, \quad n = 2, 3, 4, \ldots \quad \text{(Lyman)}$$
$$n' = 3, \quad n = 4, 5, 6 \ldots \quad \text{(Paschen)}$$
$$n' = 4, \quad n = 5, 6, 7, \ldots \quad \text{(Brackett)}$$

into the general Balmer formula (Equation 1). The relationship between these series is shown in Figure 31, B. More complex spectra are observed for the heavier elements, and, once the maze of lines is sorted out, similar equations are observed to describe these spectra. These were the data which eventually held the key to the extranuclear structure of atoms.

THE BOHR DESCRIPTION OF EXTRANUCLEAR STRUCTURE

It is clear from the picture of the atom which has been developed up to now that the extranuclear electrons will be attracted toward the positively charged nucleus. If these electrons are stationary, the system will be unstable and the electrons will be drawn into the nucleus. This simple argument suggests that the extranuclear electrons are in motion which offsets the attractive force of the nucleus. Unfortunately the fundamentals of classical electrodynamic theory lead to an impossible situation for the model of an electron rapidly moving about the nucleus. According to electrodynamics an accelerating electric charge emits electromagnetic radiation. If we assume a circular path as the simplest one that an electron may follow about the nucleus, the electron would constantly liberate energy in the form of radiation because an object moving at constant speed on a circular path is constantly accelerating. Thus, the electron would eventually lose all its energy in the form of radiation and fall into the nucleus. Any circular path would be possible, the actual path depending upon the initial conditions of formation of the atom and the length of time the system had been radiating its energy. According to this view, all atoms would be in various states of losing energy. Moreover, the radiation emitted by an atom would be of all wave lengths (energies) and would not appear as a series of sharp lines as indicated above. Niels Bohr,[1] a Danish physicist working in Rutherford's laboratory at Manchester, was the first to suggest a way out of this dilemma. BOHR describes his solution in the following words:

▼   "The way of considering a problem of this kind has, however, undergone essential alterations in recent years owing to the development of the theory of the energy radiation, and the direct affirmation of the new assumptions introduced in this theory, found by experiments on very different phenomena such as specific heats, photoelectric effect, Röntgen-rays, &c. The result of the discussion of these questions seems to be a general acknowledgment of the inadequacy of the classical electrodynamics in describing the behaviour of systems of atomic size. Whatever the alteration in the laws of motion of the electrons may be, it seems necessary to introduce in the laws in question a quantity foreign to the classical electrodynamics, i.e. Planck's constant, or as it often is called the elementary quantum of action. By the introduction of this quantity the question of the stable configuration of the electrons in the atoms is essentially changed, as this constant is of such dimensions and magnitude that it, together with the mass and charge of the particles, can determine a length of the order of magnitude required."[2]   ▲

The Photoelectric Effect and The Quantum Theory

A digression from our discussion of Bohr's theory of extranuclear atomic structure is in order at this point to discuss the concepts of the quantum theory

[1] Niels Bohr (1885–1962): Professor of Theoretical Physics at the University of Copenhagen. After taking his Ph.D. degree at the University of Copenhagen in 1911, Bohr studied for one year at Cambridge with J. J. Thomson and for one year at Manchester with Ernest Rutherford. Immediately upon his return to Copenhagen he published his famous theory for the structure of the hydrogen atom. In 1937 Bohr suggested a model for the structure of atomic nuclei. He received the Nobel Prize in physics in 1922 "for his services in the investigation of the structure of atoms, and of the radiation emanating from them."

[2] N. BOHR, "On the Constitution of Atoms and Molecules," *Philosophical Magazine*, 26, 2 (1913).

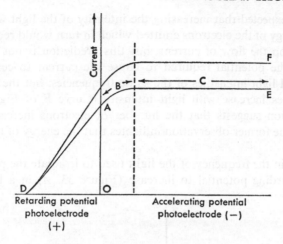

Retarding potential
photoelectrode
(+)

Accelerating potential
photoelectrode (−)

FIGURE 32

*Curve E is the current-voltage curve experimentally observed for the photo-
electric effect for light of a given frequency; Curve F represents the curve
for light of the same frequency, but of greater intensity.*

as originally suggested by Planck. Although the quantum theory can be used
to explain many phenomena in science which are difficult to understand on
the basis of classical theories, only the photoelectric effect will be presented here
for the sake of brevity.

The photoelectric effect was introduced in Chapter 2 to support the suggestion that atoms consisted in part of subatomic particles called electrons. A
quantitative study of this effect by use of an apparatus similar to that shown in
Figure 11 yields unsuspected results. Monochromatic light (i.e., light of a
single frequency) falling on electrode A causes a steady current (point A of
Figure 32) to flow through the circuit when the potential across the tube is
zero volt. Throughout this discussion it should be remembered that current
which flows in the circuit represents the electron flow through the phototube.
If the potential difference is slowly increased (with electrode A of Figure 11
negative with respect to B), a slight increase in current occurs (region B of
Figure 32), but a voltage is soon reached where there is no further increase in
current with voltage (region C of Figure 32). If the potential across the phototube is now reversed (A positive with respect to B), the electrons will be retarded by electrode B as indicated by a progressively lower current, and soon a
potential will be reached where the current will cease to flow (point D of
Figure 32). This potential is often called the retarding potential and represents
the potential required to overcome the kinetic energy of the electrons that were
emitted from the photoelectrode by the monochromatic beam of light.

It might be expected that increasing the intensity of the light would increase the kinetic energy of the electrons emitted which in turn would require a greater potential to stop the flow of current, but this prediction is not borne out by experiment. The potential required to cause the current to cease flowing is constant for all light intensities of the same frequencies, but the magnitude of the current does increase with light intensity (Curve F of Figure 32). The latter observation suggests that the number of electrons increases with light intensity, but the former observation indicates that the energy of these electrons is constant.

An increase in the frequency of the light used to irradiate the photoelectrode causes the retarding potential to increase (Figure 33, A) in a linear manner

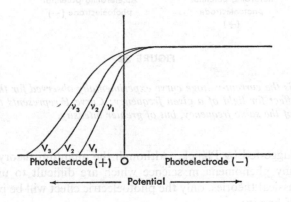

FIGURE 33, A

Curves labeled v_1, v_2, and v_3 are obtained experimentally when the frequency of light falling on a photoelectrode is increased progressively from v_1 to v_2 to v_3. At each frequency there is a corresponding retarding potential V_1, V_2, and V_3.

(Figure 33, B). It should be noted from Figure 33, B that there is a frequency below which no photoelectrons are released; i.e., no voltage is required to repel the electrons that are not released. This is often called the threshold frequency and varies with the nature of the element which is used in the construction of the photoelectrode. The threshold frequencies for some common metals are listed in Table 14. Moreover, for all elements the rate of increase of the retarding potential with frequency of the light used to excite the photoelectrons is the same; i.e., the slopes of the curves are the same value (Figure 34).

The fact that the retarding potential for a given wave length of light does not change with the intensity of the radiation is difficult to explain on the basis of classical electromagnetic theory, for it means that the kinetic energy of the

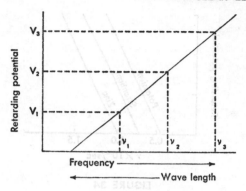

FIGURE 33, B

A plot of retarding potential versus frequency is a straight line as predicted by Equation 7.

emitted electron does not vary with the intensity of the radiation. Albert Einstein,[3] in 1905, suggested a solution to this problem by assuming that the energy associated with electromagnetic radiation comes in discrete packets or quanta which he called photons. Since the kinetic energy (as measured by the retarding potential) increased with increasing frequency, it was reasonable to suggest that the energy of the photons increased with increasing frequency of

TABLE 14

Threshold Frequencies for Some Common Metals

Metal	Threshold frequency, ($\times 10^{-13}$/sec.)	Threshold wave length, ($\times 10^{0}$ cm.)
Na	51.5	58.30
Al	63	47.70
Mg	98.5	38.20
Zn	80	37.60
Sn	83	36.20
Bi	91	33.00
Cu	100	30.00
Pt	104	28.00

[3] Albert Einstein (1879–1955): Professor of Physics at the Universities of Zurich, Prague, and Berlin, and at the Institute for Advanced Study. Born in Germany, Einstein became a Swiss citizen in 1901 and later an American citizen. He is best noted for his theory of relativity (restricted and general), the complete theory of the Brownian motion, the theory of the photoelectric effect, and the quantum theory of radiant energy. Any of these investigations would be worthy of a Nobel Prize and in 1921 he received the Nobel Prize in physics "for his services to the theory of physics, and especially for his discovery of the law of the photoelectric effect."

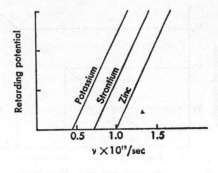

FIGURE 34

The slopes of the lines in the plot of retarding potential against the frequency of the lines are the same within experimental error for all elements. Only three elements are indicated here.

the radiation, the amount of energy per photon being equal to $h\nu$, where h is a fundamental constant of nature called Planck's constant and ν is the frequency of radiation.

Earlier Max Planck,[4] a German physicist, had shown that the distribution of frequencies found in the electromagnetic radiation emitted from a heated body could be predicted if it were assumed that any radiation has associated with it "packets of energy" (or quanta of energy) of a discrete size, the amount of energy per quantum being given by the expression

$$E = h\nu \tag{2}$$

Moreover, Planck's quantum theory assumes that it is impossible to consume or emit any fractional quanta of energy. Just as some ancient Greeks assumed that matter cannot be divided an infinite number of times and still have particles with the same characteristics, the quantum theory limits the division of radiant energy to no less than a single quantum.

Einstein employed the quantum theory to explain the photoelectric effect. If light of a certain frequency strikes a photoelectrode, an electron in the metal absorbs a photon and acquires all of the energy of the photon. By making the light more intense, more photons, all of the same energy, strike the surface; a greater number of electrons can be liberated, each having the

[4] Max Planck (1858–1947): Professor of Physics at the University of Kiel and later at Berlin. His studies of thermodynamics and of electromagnetic vibrations led him to the problem of the distribution of energy in the spectrum and to its ultimate solution in 1900. It has been said that since the time of Newton nothing has been done of greater importance than the development of Planck's famous radiation formula. In 1918 Planck received the Nobel Prize in physics "for the services rendered by him to the development of physics, by his discoveries in connection with the quantum theory."

same kinetic energy. If light of a higher frequency is allowed to fall on the photoelectrode, the energy of the photons associated with that frequency increases (as expressed by Equation 2). Electrons which absorb photons of higher energy acquire a higher kinetic energy which requires a greater retarding potential. Thus, qualitatively, the Einstein theory predicted the interrelationship between the retarding potential, the magnitude of the photoelectric current, and the frequency of the incident light beam which was experimentally observed.

A more striking proof of the validity of Einstein's theory rests in its interpretation of these relationships quantitatively. Application of the principle of the conservation of energy to this system yields the following equation

$$KE = P - W \tag{3}$$

where KE is the kinetic energy of the emitted electron, P is the energy of the photon, and W is the amount of energy required to separate an electron from the metal surface; the latter quantity is characteristic of the metal. According to Einstein's postulate the energy of the photon is given by

$$P = h\nu \tag{4}$$

and the kinetic energy of the electron is measured by the retarding potential V

$$KE = \tfrac{1}{2}mv^2 = Ve \tag{5}$$

where e represents the charge on the electron and m and v its mass and velocity, respectively. By using Equations 4 and 5, Equation 2 becomes

$$\tfrac{1}{2}mv^2 = eV = h\nu - W \tag{6}$$
or
$$V = \frac{h\nu}{e} - \frac{W}{e} \tag{7}$$

Equation 7 predicts that the retarding potential should vary linearly with the frequency of the radiation, and that the slope of this line is the quantity h/e. Because both h and e are constants and W is characteristic of the metal, a graph of V against ν for all metals should yield straight lines with the same slopes but with different intercepts. These are precisely the experimental results that are obtained! Moreover, the value for Planck's constant, h, as derived from the experimental slopes of the graphs shown in Figure 34, is in good agreement with the values obtained by other widely diverse experiments. Thus, the key hypothesis in the quantum theory as applied by Einstein, and by Planck before him, is that radiation is absorbed or emitted in quanta, the amount of energy per quantum being related to the frequency of the radiation according to Equation 1.

BOHR also invoked the concept of the quantum of energy to explain atomic structure.

▼   "Now the essential point in Planck's theory of radiation is that the energy radiation from an atomic system does not take place in the continuous way assumed in the ordinary electrodynamics, but that it, on the contrary, takes place in distinctly separated emissions, the amount of energy radiated out from an atomic vibrator of frequency v in a single emission being equal to $\tau h v$, where τ is an entire number, and h is a universal constant."[5]   ▲

Bohr's Postulates

It was assumed that the extranuclear electrons revolved about the nucleus in circular orbits, and, in BOHR's own words, that

▼   "1) An atomic system possesses a number of states in which no emission of energy radiation takes place, even if the particles are in motion relative to each other, and such an emission is to be expected on ordinary electrodynamics. The states are denoted as 'stationary' states of the system under consideration.

"2) Any emission or absorption of energy radiation will correspond to the transition between two stationary states. The radiation emitted during such a transition is homogeneous and the frequency v is determined by the relation $hv = A_1 - A_2$ where h is Planck's constant and A_1 and A_2 are the energies of the system in the two stationary states.

"3) That the dynamical equilibrium of the system in the stationary states is governed by the ordinary laws of mechanics while these laws do not hold for the transition of one state to another."[6]   ▲

These postulates permitted Bohr to describe quantitatively the simplest atomic system, the hydrogen atom (Figure 35). The first postulate assured that the electron would not radiate its energy and slow up as long as it remained in a certain orbit about the nucleus. This postulate is in direct opposition to classical electrodynamics. The second postulate provided the theoretical basis for the calculation of the energies of the lines observed in the hydrogen spectrum. The quantum theory was introduced into BOHR's atomic theory as the so-called "quantum condition."

[5] "On the Constitution of Atoms and Molecules," p. 4.
[6] N. BOHR, "On the Quantum Theory of Radiation and the Structure of the Atom," *Philosophical Magazine*, **30**, 396 (1915).

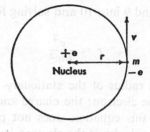

FIGURE 35

The Bohr model of a hydrogen atom assumes that an electron with charge −e and mass m revolves about the nucleus with charge +e. Bohr further assumed that the electron is moving with a velocity v in a circular path.

▼ "In any atomic or molecular system consisting of positive nuclei and electrons in which the nuclei are at rest relative to each other, and the electrons move in circular orbits, the angular momentum of each electron round the centre of its orbit will be equal to $h/2\pi$ in the 'normal' state of the system, i.e., the state in which the total energy is a <u>minimum.</u>"[7] ▲

In other words, the angular momentum of the electron in any orbit could be only $h/2\pi$ or any whole multiple of this value.

According to Bohr's second and third postulates the motion of an electron in an orbit can be described by the ordinary laws of mechanics. For example, in the case of the hydrogen atom the electrostatic attraction of the nucleus for the electron is counterbalanced by the centripetal force of the electron. This situation is described by Bohr for the hydrogen atom (Figure 35).

According to Bohr's third postulate the centripetal force (F_c) and the electrostatic attraction (F_e) between the nucleus and the electron can be calculated from Newton's laws of motion and Coulomb's law, respectively, for any stationary state as

$$F_c = ma = m\frac{v^2}{r} \tag{8}$$

$$F_e = \frac{(-e)(e)}{r^2} \tag{9}$$

where m, a, and v represent the mass, acceleration, and velocity, respectively, of an electron with charge e moving about the nucleus in a circular orbit of radius r (cf. Figure 35). For any stationary state

$$F_c + F_e = 0 \tag{10}$$

[7] *Ibid.*

Substituting Equations 8 and 9 into 10 and solving for r

$$r = \frac{e^2}{mv^2} \tag{11}$$

Equation 11 describes the radius of the stationary state in terms of a single variable, the velocity of the electron; the charge and mass of the electron are constants. Unfortunately this equation does not permit us to calculate the radius of an orbit since the velocity of the electron in a given orbit is unknown.

However, Bohr's quantum condition for the angular momentum of an electron in any orbit provides the key to the solution of this problem.

$$\text{angular momentum} = nh/2\pi \tag{12}$$

The angular momentum (Equation 13) for an electron moving about the nucleus in a circular orbit can be obtained from Newton's laws of motion.

$$\text{angular momentum} = mvr \tag{13}$$

Combining Equations 12 and 13

$$\frac{nh}{2\pi} = mvr \tag{14}$$

Eliminating v from Equations 11 and 14 and solving for r

$$r = n^2 \left[\frac{h^2}{4\pi^2 e^2 m} \right] \tag{15}$$

Equation 15 permits the calculation of the allowed orbits in the Bohr picture of the atom. All the quantities within the brackets are constants which can be determined by independent experiments. It should be recalled that n represents an integer, and it is called the principal quantum number. Thus, the radius of the first stationary state is given by $n = 1$, the second state by $n = 2$, the third state by $n = 3$, etc. Inserting the values for the quantities (in compatible units) within the brackets in Equation 15 the radius of the stationary states are given by

$$r = n^2 \, 0.53 \times 10^{-8} \, \text{cm.} \tag{16}$$

The radii for the first five allowed orbits ($n = 1, 2, 3, 4, 5$) are listed in Table 15. A variety of modern experimental techniques gives estimates of about 0.5×10^{-8} cm. for the radius of the hydrogen atom. This is in very good agreement with the value calculated for the first Bohr orbit ($n = 1$) and lends support to Bohr's description of atomic structure.

TABLE 15

The Radii for the First Five Allowed Bohr
Orbits for the Hydrogen Atom (Calculated
from Equation 16)

Principal quantum number	Radius ($\times 10^8$) cm.
1	0.53
2	2.12
3	4.77
4	8.48
5	13.25

A consideration of the energy of a stationary state (Figure 35) led Bohr to a theoretical description of the spectrum of hydrogen. The total energy A_n of an electron in a stationary state n is the sum of its kinetic energy KE and potential energy P. According to Bohr's third postulate, these quantities can also be obtained from Newton's laws of motion and Coulomb's law of electrostatic attraction.

$$A_n = P + KE \tag{17}$$

$$KE = \tfrac{1}{2}mv^2 \tag{18}$$

$$P = \frac{(-e)(e)}{r} \tag{19}$$

$$A_n = -\frac{e^2}{r} + \frac{1}{2}mv^2 \tag{20}$$

Solving Equation 11 for mv^2, substituting this value into Equation 20, and then substituting the value of r from Equation 15 into the result gives

$$A_n = -\frac{1}{n^2}\left[\frac{2\pi^2 e^4 m}{h^2}\right] \tag{21}$$

That is, the total energy of an electron in any stationary state can be calculated from a collection of fundamental constants.

The Hydrogen Spectrum

Bohr's second postulate and Equation 21 provided the means for the interpretation of the spectrum of hydrogen. Suppose the electron in the hydrogen atom is in the smallest allowed orbit ($n = 1$), and that enough energy is supplied to raise the electron to the next allowed orbit ($n = 2$). The energy for the electron in each of these orbits can be calculated from Equation 21, and the difference in energy between these two orbits is the energy which must be supplied to make this transition from one orbit to the next.

The spectrum of hydrogen (or any atom) arises because the hydrogen atoms are excited by an external source of energy. It is assumed that at room temperature the overwhelming majority of the atoms have their electrons in the first allowed orbit ($n = 1$). Upon excitation, some electrons acquire enough energy to put them into the second Bohr orbit ($n = 2$), while others are excited to higher orbits ($n = 3, 4, 5$, etc.). Thus, the electrons are randomly excited from the first Bohr orbit (or the ground state) to all other possible states. According to Bohr's second postulate, after excitation the electrons drop back to the ground state, emitting radiation equivalent to the difference in energy between the two states involved in the transition. The energy difference can be calculated by the previously outlined procedure.

Suppose that an electron is in an orbit ($n = n'$) other than the first allowed orbit ($n = 1$). According to the second Bohr postulate when the electron returns to the ground state the energy liberated is $A_{n'} - A_1$, and this energy appears as radiation of a certain frequency ν.

$$h\nu = A_{n'} - A_1 \tag{22}$$

Substituting the total energy of the electron in each state, given by Equation 21, into Equation 22 gives

$$\nu = \left[\frac{2\pi^2 m e^4}{h^3}\right]\left[\frac{1}{1^2} - \frac{1}{n'^2}\right] \tag{23}$$

Equation 23 represents the triumph of the Bohr quantum theory. It is qualitatively similar to the formula which describes the Lyman series of lines (Equation 1 and Figure 31, B) observed in the hydrogen spectrum. Moreover, it predicts that the Rydberg constant, R, is equal to the factor $2\pi^2 m e^4 / h^3$ which is composed of quantities that are all fundamental constants. Using the "best values" for these quantities (in compatible units) the theoretical value of the Rydberg constant is 109,750. The difference between the theoretical value and the experimentally determined value (page 92) is less than 0.1 per cent!

An extension of these arguments showed that the other series of lines in the hydrogen spectrum corresponded to excited electrons returning to the second Bohr orbit ($n = 2$, Balmer series) and to the third Bohr orbit ($n = 3$, Brackett series) from higher orbits. For each series of lines, Equation 1 is equivalent to the corresponding form of Equation 23. The quantitative results deduced from the Bohr theory for the hydrogen atom are given in Figure 36. The nucleus of the atom is negligibly small compared to the allowed orbits, and the propor-

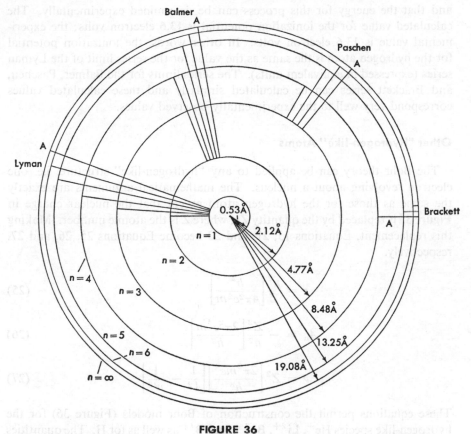

FIGURE 36

The spectral lines observed for hydrogen atoms occur because electrons which have been excited to higher energy levels than the ground state return to the ground state with the liberation of energy. Transitions designated by (A) represent the series limit, and for the Lyman series this limit also corresponds to the ionization potential of the hydrogen atom.

tions in Figure 36 are not to be taken literally, although the numbers quoted are correct. The orbits come closer and closer together, and the outer circle represents the orbit in which the electron is essentially free from the attraction of the nucleus. The energy (expressed in frequency units) of the electron when it is in the orbit designated $n = \infty$ can be approximated by substituting a large number for n (e.g. 1000) in Equation 23 or in Equation 1. This is the energy required to remove an electron from the ground state ($n = 1$) to a distance where it is not influenced by the nuclear charge. It should be recalled that this corresponds to the ionization of an atom,

$$H \rightarrow H^+ + e^- \tag{24}$$

and that the energy for this process can be determined experimentally. The calculated value for the ionization potential is 13.6 electron volts; the experimental value is 13.6 electron volts. In other words, the ionization potential for the hydrogen atom is the same as the value for the series limit of the Lyman series (expressed in equivalent units). The series limits for the Balmer, Paschen, and Brackett series can be calculated similarly and these calculated values correspond very well to the experimentally observed values.

Other "Hydrogen-like" Atoms

The Bohr theory can be applied to any "hydrogen-like" structure, i.e. one electron revolving about a nucleus. The mathematical arguments are exactly the same as those for the hydrogen atom except that the nuclear charge in Figure 35 is replaced by the quantity Ze, where Z is the atomic number. Making this replacement, Equations 15, 21, and 23 become Equations 25, 26, and 27, respectively.

$$r = \frac{n^2}{Z}\left[\frac{h^2}{4\pi^2e^2m}\right] \tag{25}$$

$$A_n = -\frac{Z^2}{n^2}\left[\frac{2\pi^2e^4m}{h^2}\right] \tag{26}$$

$$\nu = Z^2\left[\frac{2\pi^2me^4}{h^3}\right]\left[\frac{1}{1^2} - \frac{1}{n'^2}\right] \tag{27}$$

These equations permit the construction of Bohr models (Figure 36) for the hydrogen-like species He^+, Li^{2+}, Be^{3+}, and B^{4+} as well as for H. The quantities calculated by Equations 25, 26, and 27 are related to the corresponding numerical values by the nuclear charge on the species. For example, energy radiated for the transition of an electron from $n = \infty$ to $n = 1$ which corresponds to the ionization potential can be calculated from Equation 27 for "hydrogen-like" atoms; a comparison of the calculated values and the experimental values (Table 16) indicates a striking agreement between these two values. Moreover, the spectra for "hydrogen-like" elements shows the lines predicted by Equation 27.

The Bohr theory was an outstanding success in describing "hydrogen-like" atoms, but it failed to account for the spectrum of any atoms or ions with more than one electron. As interest grew in spectroscopic measurements and the techniques became more and more precise, facts which could not be explained by the simple Bohr theory were uncovered. For example, many of the lines which were predicted by the Bohr theory were shown to consist of several closely spaced lines. If the quantum theory is correct, this observation implied that in some cases there exist allowed orbits that were almost identical in energy. Suppose that instead of one Bohr orbit at $n = 2$ there were two orbits

TABLE 16

*Ionization Potentials in Electron Volts
for Hydrogen-like Systems*

Nuclear charge	Hydrogen-like atom	Calculated ionization potential	Observed ionization potential
1	H	13.6	13.6
2	He⁺	54.2	54.5
3	Li²⁺	122	122
4	Be³⁺	217	218
5	B⁴⁺	339	340

of very similar energies (Figure 37). Electrons could be excited into either of these upper orbits, and when they returned to the ground state they would re-emit this energy as radiation. However, two closely spaced lines would appear in the spectrum; one corresponding to the transition of an electron from the upper energy level for $n = 2$ to the ground state and one from the lower energy level to the ground state.

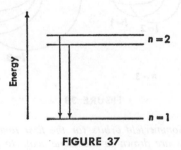

FIGURE 37

Two orbits of very similar energies give two closely spaced lines. This situation is indicated diagrammatically by using an energy level diagram. In studying diagrams of this type it should be remembered that only the vertical axis is important. The distance between two energy levels represents the difference in the energy of these levels.

Modification of the Bohr Description

In 1916 the German scientist Arnold Sommerfeld modified the Bohr theory to account for the newly observed structure of some spectral lines. Sommerfeld showed that elliptical orbits with the nucleus at a focus were possible as well as the original Bohr circular orbits. The quantum condition restricts the electron to certain allowed ellipses, and, since the size of an ellipse is determined by two factors (the lengths of the major and minor axis), two quantum numbers were introduced. It will be recalled that Bohr's original quantum number,

n (the principal quantum number), reflected the radius of a circular orbit. Sommerfeld introduced a second quantum number, l, the secondary quantum number, which was a measure of the "flatness" of the ellipse; the modified theory restricted the values of l to be integers and dependent on the value of n.

$$l = 0, 1, 2, 3, \ldots (n - 1) \tag{28}$$

From Equation 28 it follows that for each principal quantum number there are n allowed orbits (n values of l); $n = 1$ has one allowed orbit, $n = 2$ has two allowed orbits, etc. The most elliptical orbit for a given value of n occurs for $l = 0$ and the orbits become more circular until $l = (n - 1)$ (Figure 38). Sommerfeld showed that the orbits associated with a given principal quantum number have slightly different energies, and this led to the prediction (which was verified by observation) that certain lines in the spectrum should be multiple lines.

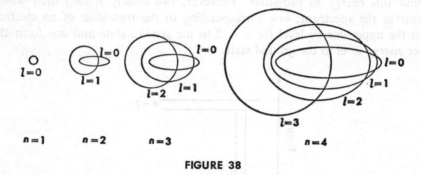

FIGURE 38

The possible Bohr-Sommerfeld orbits for the first four principal quantum numbers. All orbits are drawn to the same scale to present the correct relative sizes.

The allowed orbits in the Bohr-Sommerfeld theory were not restricted to two dimensions, but it was shown that the plane of the orbits could have only a certain orientation in space, and this orientation was designated by a third quantum number, m_l. For the sake of simplicity we shall discuss the possible orientations of a circular orbit corresponding to a given principal quantum number, although it should be emphasized that this argument can be used for elliptical orbits also. An electron revolving in the circular orbit ($l = 2$), which corresponds to the third principal quantum number ($n = 3$), in the direction indicated in Figure 39 is equivalent to a current flowing in a circular wire, and a magnetic field is established in the direction indicated by the arrow. If this system is placed in an external magnetic field, it will line itself up so that the generated magnetic field is in the same direction as the external field, much the

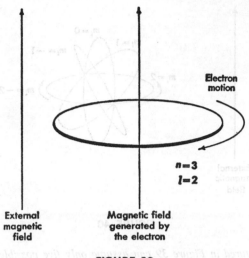

n=3
l=2

External
magnetic
field

Magnetic field
generated by
the electron

Electron
motion

FIGURE 39

The electron moving in an orbit is equivalent to a current flowing in a wire.
The electron motion results in the generation of a magnetic field. The orbit
shown is for an electron with n = 3 and n = 2.

same as when a compass needle lines itself up with the earth's magnetic field.
Thus, the plane of the orbit is perpendicular to the direction of the external
field, and to move this plane to a different position with respect to the magnetic
field requires energy. Sommerfeld showed that there are only certain allowed
positions which the plane of the orbit may take, and the number of orientations
depended upon the quantum number l.

$$\text{number of orientations} = 2l + 1 \qquad (29)$$

For the case illustrated in Figure 39 there are five possible orientations (Figure
40). These slightly different energy states which appear under the influence of
a magnetic field are designated by a third quantum number, m_l, called the
magnetic quantum number. The values of m_l are integral and depend upon
the values of l.

$$m_l = l, (l-1), (l-2)\ldots 0 \ldots -1, -2, -(l-1), -l \qquad (30)$$

In Figure 40 it might appear that the orientations labeled $m_l = 2$ and $m_l = -2$
are the same; these are actually different orientations since the electron is
revolving about the nucleus in opposite directions. The possible orientations
of the orbital plane are necessary to explain the observed splitting of certain
spectral lines under the influence of an external magnetic field (the Zeeman
effect). The energy for a transition of an electron from a higher energy state

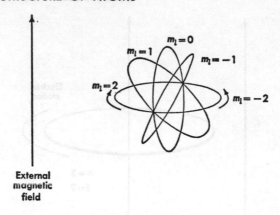

FIGURE 40

*The orbit pictured in Figure 39 can assume only five possible orientations
with respect to an external magnetic field.*

which may have certain allowed orientations of the orbital plane would appear
as a single spectral line in the absence of a magnetic field. Upon application
of a magnetic field the transition would occur between slightly different energy
states depending upon the orientation of the orbital plane in the magnetic
field, and the original energy state would be split into several closely spaced
states (Figure 41). The existence of several closely spaced energy states in the
presence of a magnetic field would lead directly to the splitting of certain spectral lines.

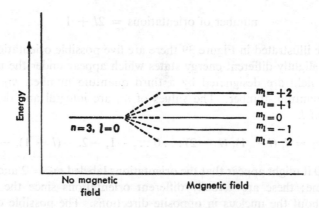

FIGURE 41

*The transitions which arise because of the possible orientations of the
orbitals illustrated in Figure 40 are shown on this energy level diagram.*

The relationship between the quantum numbers for the first four allowed states discussed to this point appears in Table 17. In accord with the argu-

TABLE 17

The Relationship between the Principal, Secondary,
and Magnetic Quantum Numbers

Principal quantum number, n	Secondary quantum number, l from Equation 28	Magnetic quantum number, m_l from Equation 30
1	0	0
2	0	0
	1	$+1, 0, -1$
3	0	0
	1	$+1, 0, -1$
	2	$+2, +1, 0, -1, -2$
4	0	0
	1	$+1, 0, -1$
	2	$+2, +1, 0, -1, -2$
	3	$+3, +2, +1, 0, -1, -2, -3$

ments previously presented for each value of the principal quantum number, there are n integral values of the secondary quantum from $l = 0$ to $l = n - 1$; for each value of the secondary quantum number there are $2l + 1$ integral values of the magnetic quantum number from $m_l = -1$ to $m_l = +1$.

The energies of the various stationary states are summarized in Figure 42. Diagrams of this type are called energy level diagrams and represent the energies of the various allowed orbits (allowed energy states) with respect to each other. The characteristic lines in the spectrum of hydrogen, for example, appear because the electrons which are excited from the ground state ($n = 1$) to higher energy levels by the application of an external source of energy fall back to the ground state re-emitting this energy in discrete amounts as radiation in accordance with the Bohr frequency condition (Equation 23).

The magnetic quantum number was introduced because certain spectral lines were split into a greater number of lines when the atom was placed in a magnetic field, but some spectral lines were found to have an additional fine structure in the absence of a magnetic field also. That is, some lines, when recorded with high resolution spectrometers, appear as a series of closely spaced lines. Since the spectral lines arise because of the transition of electrons between various orbits, this observation implies that there are two energy states for the electron that are very similar in energy. An electron in energy state A of Figure 43 will give rise to a spectral line when it returns to the lower energy state C; the energy of the spectral line is equivalent to a. On the other hand, an electron in energy state B gives rise to a different spectral line when it returns to the lower energy state, and the energy of this transition is b. Thus, for this system, two spectral lines will appear with a difference in wave length (energy) which corresponds to Δ, the difference in energy between the energy states A

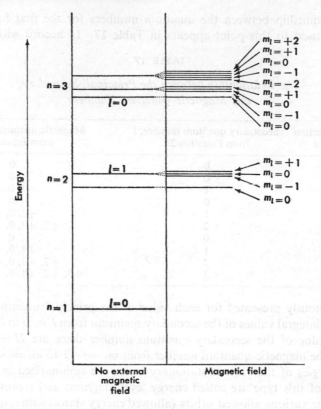

FIGURE 42

An energy level diagram showing the relationship of the various quantum numbers.

and B. The occurrence of this type of fine structure for certain spectral lines could not be explained on the basis of the Bohr theory even as modified by Sommerfeld. These splittings are very small and are not to be confused with the splitting caused by a magnetic field.

The answer to this puzzle was suggested in 1925 by two Dutch physicists, Uhlenbeck and Goudsmit, who assumed that the electron, as it rotates about the nucleus, also spins on its own axis. Suppose an electron (A of Figure 44) was moving in a given Bohr orbit. This orbital motion is equivalent to the passage of an electric current in a coil of wire and generates a magnetic field in the direction C according to classical electromagnetic theory. If the electron (for example A) is also rotating on its axis, this is also equivalent to a current moving in a coil; the magnetic field in the case of electron A is in the opposite direction to that of the magnetic field due to the orbital motion. It is apparent

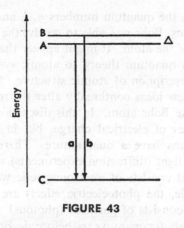

FIGURE 43

A difference in the sense of electron spin gives rise to two slightly different energies.

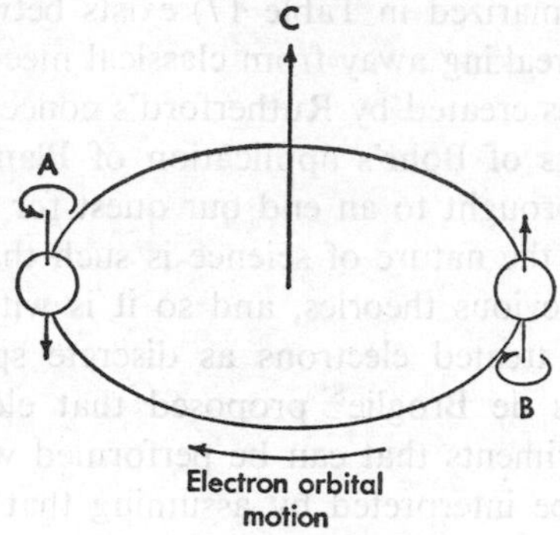

FIGURE 44

A pictorial representation of the effect of electron spin on the magnetic field due to orbital motion.

that the electron can rotate also in the opposite sense (*B* of Figure 44), and in this case the magnetic field is in the same direction as that field created by the orbital motion. Uhlenbeck and Goudsmit assigned an angular momentum to the spinning electron. Only two quantum numbers ($+\frac{1}{2}$ or $-\frac{1}{2}$) are used to designate electron spin since the electron can spin in only one direction (*A*) or another (*B*). The difference in the two possible electron spins corresponds to a slight difference in energy for the electron. A small amount of work is required to change the orientation of the electron spin from *A* to *B*. Thus, the electron spinning as indicated in *A*, Figure 44, is slightly lower in energy than the electron spinning as indicated in *B*. If a valence electron in a low energy state is excited to a higher state, so that it is spinning as in *A* of Figure 44, it will give rise to radiation of less energy when it falls back to the ground state than if it had been excited and were spinning as in *B* of Figure 44. However, the excitation of electrons is a random process, and there are as many electrons excited to spin in *A* as in *B*, and two spectral lines appear.

To recapitulate, the modified Bohr theory thus explains the spectrum of the elements by allowing (quantizing) only certain motions of the electrons about the nucleus. The relative energies of the electron in each of these allowed motions can be designated by a quantum number. The main spectral lines arise from the restriction of electrons to certain allowed orbits, and the splitting of certain spectral lines by a magnetic field occurs because of the preferred orientation of the orbital planes in space. The fact that some spectral lines have a fine structure is attributed to the two possible spins of the electron. Although the discussion in this chapter has not been developed by using rigorous mathematical arguments, it can be shown that a simple relationship (summarized in Table 17) exists between the quantum numbers n, l, and m_l. By breaking away from classical mechanics, Bohr was able to resolve the difficulties created by Rutherford's concept of the atom. It might appear that the results of Bohr's application of Planck's quantum theory to atomic systems has brought to an end our quest for a description of atomic structure. However, the nature of science is such that new ideas continually alter the results of previous theories, and so it is with the Bohr atom. In this discussion we have treated electrons as discrete spheres of electrical charge, but in 1924 Louis de Broglie[8] proposed that electrons have a dual nature. There are experiments that can be performed with light (diffraction experiments) which can be interpreted by assuming that light consists of electromagnetic waves; however, other experiments (for example, the photoelectric effect) are best interpreted on the assumption that light consists of particles (photons). This philosophical dilemma had faced physicists for many years before de Broglie suggested that matter could also have a dual nature.

Einstein showed that a relationship exists between the energy E of a photon and its frequency ν.

$$E = h\nu \qquad (31)$$

Frequency is normally associated with wave motion, but the energy of a particle can be expressed in terms of its mass and velocity. According to Einstein's theory of relativity, the energy of a photon of mass m moving at the speed of light c is given by

$$E = mc^2 \qquad (32)$$

Combining Equations 31 and 32 gives Equation 33

$$\frac{h\nu}{c} = mc \qquad (33)$$

But since the frequency of the radiation and its wave length λ are related by

$$\nu\lambda = c, \quad \text{or} \quad \lambda = \frac{c}{\nu} \qquad (34)$$

combining Equations 34 and 33 gives Equation 35

$$\lambda = \frac{h}{mc} \qquad (35)$$

That is, a photon of mass m has associated with it a wave length λ! de Broglie suggested that Equation 35 could describe the wave length of a particle moving

---

[8] Prince Louis Victor de Broglie (1892–   ): Member of an illustrious old French family. de Broglie received the Nobel Prize in physics in 1929 "for his discovery of the wave character of electrons."

at any velocity, and three years later this suggestion was confirmed experimentally by Davisson and Germer. These investigators were able to measure the "wave length" of electrons moving with known velocities.

The results of de Broglie's suggestion have had far-reaching consequences in the realm of atomic physics since the electrons which move about the nucleus of an atom must be treated as possessing wave nature. Although the mathematics required to solve this problem are too involved to be considered here, it should be pointed out that the results of these calculations agree in general with those of the more simple Bohr concept.

SUGGESTED READING

Einstein, A., and Infeld, L. *The Evolution of Physics*, Chapter IV, "Quanta." New York: Simon and Schuster, Inc., 1938.

Gilreath, E. S. *Fundamental Concepts of Inorganic Chemistry*, Chapter 2. New York: McGraw-Hill Book Company, Inc., 1958.

Haas, A. *The World of Atoms*. London: D. Van Nostrand Company, Inc., 1928. Ten non-mathematical lectures on atomic structure.

Hoffmann, B. *The Strange Story of the Quantum*. New York: Dover Publications, Inc., 1959. A very readable, non-mathematical account of the revolution in physics which led to the quantum theory.

Wheeler, P. D. "The Reality of the Atom," *Journal of Chemical Education*, **4**, 327 (1927).

CHAPTER 6

The Epilogue

The course of this story has touched on many fields of investigation some of which may not have seemed particularly related — or relevant — on first thought, but each has contributed to our understanding of atomic structure. The empirical relationships or laws such as the radioactive decay series, the Balmer formulation for the spacing of spectral lines, the scattering of α-particles by matter, and the photoelectric effect are all readily explained by assuming the existence of atoms with the characteristics described in the preceding chapters. In attempting to trace the development of the modern atom several other points concerning the nature of science have been illustrated indirectly and these are now discussed explicitly.

Our present concept of the atom has resulted from the solution of successive problems. In general these problems were gradually recognized, each apparently waiting its turn for formulation and subsequent solution. To be certain, some important observations were made before their significance was realized, but these too had to await their turn in the succession of events. Each contribution to the theory of atomic structure modified the then existing theory and was in turn modified to conform with still newer experimental results.

The origins of the atomic theory are found in a system of philosophy which started in Greece, but the evidence on which proof rests for the existence of the atom and its detailed structure has been gathered in relatively recent times. It is apparent that most of the evidence which has been used in support of the present atomic model is of an indirect nature, but this is not surprising when the relation of the physical dimensions of atoms to the limitations of the instruments available for direct observations are considered.

The current model of the atom has been used to predict certain relationships which were later verified experimentally, and it is this complementary nature of experiment and theory that has led to the statement that this model "explains" the experimental observations. A word of caution is necessary for those not versed in the vernacular of science when they consider the meaning of a scientific "explanation." By assuming that atoms exist, that they have a certain gross structure, that the nucleus contains a predictable distribution of protons and neutrons, and that the electrons are distributed about the nucleus in the manner described in earlier chapters, we are led by a series of logical arguments to understand and interrelate many independent experimental observations. Equally apparent is the fact that we have not explained *why* atoms exist, *why* electric charges interact with each other in the way that they do, *why* electrons can exist only in certain energy levels, or *why* electrons can behave as waves or as particles. These questions belong more properly to the realm of philosophy which differs from the physical sciences in the nature of the "tools" employed for arriving at answers to such questions. There is no implication here that a scientist cannot be a philosopher. Indeed, some scientists succeed as philosophers, but many others are not aware of the philosophic implications of their work.

A question as to the "reality" of atoms often arises in the minds of those who are bothered by their inability to "see" atoms. That bit of matter which is called an atom does not depend upon the human mind for its existence (as does, for example, the concept of democracy). Atoms have characteristic properties associated with them, just as does any object. For example, by observing the sounds (and odors!) emanating from a barn one can conclude without entering the structure that it houses a herd of goats — and not horses or cows. None of the known properties of atoms permits their detection directly by any of the human senses, and, therefore, scientists must rely on techniques employing indirect observations such as those described in this volume. Thus, even though we cannot escape the conclusion that atoms exist, their "observation" is difficult. The very fact that the character ascribed to the atom has been modified through the years to incorporate the most recent experimental results should restrain us from believing that the current description is a final picture of the "true atom" any more than was Dalton's concept of the atom in 1820. To be certain, the present model is more refined and undoubtedly more correct than Dalton's, but this should not delude us into thinking that there is no need for further study or investigation. Scientists are strange creatures; they strive to construct theories to explain experimental results and then they spend an equivalent amount of time and effort performing experiments which sorely test the validity of their newly constructed theories.

The atomic model presented here has been used to explain the results of many experiments, but equally important is the fact that it predicts an electronic structure for each element which provides a basis for understanding the experimentally observed chemical and physical properties of the elements. The chemical properties of an element are primarily dependent upon the number and characteristics of the outermost (or valence) electrons, whereas certain physical properties (atomic radius, ionization potential, electron affinity, etc.)

are dependent upon the extent to which extranuclear electrons exist about the nucleus. With the principles discussed in this volume it is possible to establish the number of extranuclear electrons and their orbital distribution about the nucleus for any atom. The correlations between the predicted electronic structures and the observed properties of the elements are a logical extension of the subject presented here and an engrossing study in itself, but, unfortunately, not within the scope of this volume.

INDEX

Alpha-particle scattering, 72
Alpha-rays:
    equivalence to He^{++}, 51, 54
    nature of, 42, 44
Aristotle, 2
Aston, Francis William, 66
Atom, as distinguished from molecule, 10
Atomic model:
    Kelvin-Thomson, 67–71
    nuclear, 73
    Rutherford, 73–77
Atomic number, determination of, 80–82
Atomic theory:
    Bohr's, 94, 100–102
    Dalton's, 4–5
    earliest concepts, 1–4
Atomic weights:
    Avogadro's method for calculating, 10–12
    Dalton's relative, 7
Avogadro, Amadeo, 9
Avogadro's hypothesis, 9–12

Bacon, Francis, 2
Balmer series, 92–93
Becquerel, Henri, 36–38
Berthollet, Claude Louis, 3
Beta-rays, nature of, 43–44
Bohr, Niels, 94
Bohr's orbit, radius of, 102–103
Bohr's postulates, 100–102
Bohr-Sommerfeld theory, 107–112
Boltwood, Bertram Borden, 55
Brackett series, 93
Broglie, Louis Victor de, 114

Canal rays: 24–28
    detection of, 25
    e/m for, 26–28
Cathode ray tube, 14–15
Cathode rays: 13–24
    deflection by electric field, 18–19
    deflection by magnetic field, 15–16
    detection of, 15
    e/m for, 21–23
    nature of, 17, 114
    source of, 24
Chadwick, James, 87
Crookes, William, 14
Curie, Marie Sklodowska, 39
Curie, Pierre, 39

Dalton, John, 4
Dalton's atomic theory, 4–5
Democritus, 2

Edison, Thomas Alva, 28
Einstein, Albert, 97
Electron spin, 112–113
Electrons, *see* Cathode rays
Electroscope, 15–17
Element, early definition of, 3
Elliptical orbits, 107–108
Extranuclear electronic structure, 93–94

Fajans, Kasimir, 58
Faraday, Michael, 22
Fleck, Alexander, 56

Gamma-rays, 40
Gaseous discharge, 13–16
Gassendi, Pierre, 3
Gay-Lussac, Joseph Louis, 8
Geiger, Hans, 48
Goldstein, E., 24

119